IT'S NOT ABOUT THE SEX

Teresa,

Enjoy the read.

John DiGiolam

IT'S NOT ABOUT THE SEX

JOHN DIGIROLAMO

TESTIMONIALS

"Bringing awareness to the public, the book is a must-read for everyone. From the beautiful suburbs to small country towns, the stories accurately portray the horrors of human trafficking happening right under our noses."

Breahannah Leary, Survivor of Human Sex Trafficking

"Everyone needs to read this book. Human traffickers are truly hunting their prey, the innocent and the desperate. Educating ourselves and others is the only way we will stop them and make our communities safer."

Beth Ritchie, Director of BV HOPE

"With *It's Not About the Sex*, author John DiGirolamo pulls back the curtain on sex trafficking and sexual addiction and abuse in America. These stories, from first-hand accounts of those involved and affected, are tragic and horrifying. DiGirolamo exposes a world of dark addiction, despair, and human brutality . . . a world that is all around us, but often unseen. But shining through these testimonies are also stories of triumph, faith, and redemption. An excellent, eye-opening read, that will hopefully bring more attention to this difficult topic."

Dean Morgan, Chief of Police, Buena Vista Police Department

"*It's Not About the Sex* provides tremendous insight into the grossly unacknowledged evils of the domestic sex-trafficking industry. Moving quickly through real-life testimonies, the text submerges the reader into the emotions, pain, and brokenness of this reality while simultaneously highlighting the true hope of rescue, recovery, and restoration for survivors."

Anonymous Advocate

"*It's Not About the Sex* highlights the uncomfortable and taboo topic of human sex trafficking–something many believe could not plague their own homes or communities, which could not be further from the truth. The four unique stories told by law enforcement, a brothel owner, survivor, and advocate detail the enormous emotional, relational and physical plight this issue has on those involved. Even more meaningful is the healing in these stories, and how the deep impact of trauma and shame can be healed. This is an emotional, educational and eye-opening book that will surely drive the reader to purpose and provide new insight into this dark and disturbing problem."

Katherine E. Kuhlman, Psy.D., ABPP, Owner and Chief Psychologist, Kuhlman Psychology & Consulting Board Certified in Police and Public Safety Psychology

"Powerful, brutal, and explosive, Mr. DiGirolamo's exposé on sex trafficking in Colorado is compelling and timely. The brutal stories of young girls being lured/forced into this slavery must be told. For some reason, the mainstream media avoids this issue at all costs. The occasional 'exposé' by a local TV station may pop up but the sheer magnitude of this horror is ignored. These stories will break your heart. But maybe that is what it will take for society to take some action. Read this book to see what our society is up against. Then demand action."

George Gramlich, Editor, the *Sangre de Cristo Sentinel*, Westcliffe, Colorado

"This is not the book to pick up if you want an easy read. It will make you uncomfortable. It will tear at you. It will help you to understand what millions of people live through as they are trafficked. And once you've read this, you will find that you want–you must–do something to fight trafficking."

Sues Hess, Reclaiming Hope, Executive Director

It's Not About the Sex

True Stories of Human Trafficking from a Law Enforcement Officer, a Survivor, a Brothel Madam, and an Advocate

John DiGirolamo

Published by www.ItIsNotAbout.com

ISBN: 979-8-9862474-0-3

CONTENTS

DEDICATION

This book is dedicated to all those seeking
to end human trafficking, especially survivors,
advocates, and law enforcement.

It's also dedicated to my daughters,
Nicole and Megan, who are making a
positive difference in their communities
through their work.

PREFACE

All the stories are based on real events. The author collaborated and reviewed the contents with each person profiled in the chapter to ensure accuracy and authenticity. Details for context and illustrative purposes were added where necessary. Some dates and locations have been altered to shield identities. Also, the names of the accused, criminals, and witnesses have been changed in some instances to protect both the innocent and the guilty.

This book contains quotes and references to pop culture as an integral part of the storytelling. Some song lyrics appear in the book to demonstrate how our modern culture feeds into human exploitation, especially degrading to women as included in the law enforcement chapter.

Some of the material contained in this book is for mature audiences.

INTRODUCTION

It's Not About the Sex features true stories of human trafficking so ordinary citizens will become more aware of how this problem occurs under the radar in our society. The stories are not salacious or graphic, but they do accurately describe the horrors of human trafficking.

Before writing this book, I was peripherally aware of human trafficking, believing it only occurred on our country's border or in large cities. The various circumstances detailed are based on real-life experiences and are all too common. Unfortunately, human trafficking is pervasive throughout this country and the world. I decided to write stories that occurred primarily in rural and suburban America because many people are surprised to find out it exists in idyllic small towns and "nice" communities in addition to our larger cities.

Many people are surprised to learn that 85 percent of those trafficked are born in the US and 60 percent of exploited children are recruited by their peers. Only 5 percent of those trafficked are kidnapped, and 10 percent of pimps are women. It's not always obvious when someone is trafficked and it's common that the individual is in denial. Victims can be seen by human services, the police, or some other government agency as many as nine times and still not be identified as a victim of human trafficking.

The personal accounts in this book are based on actual events and haven't been over-sensationalized. They do, however, provide an authentic glimpse into the evil hiding in plain sight within our neighborhoods.

Just as important as the stories are the tips I've included so you can help stop human trafficking. It is well within our capacity to inform others about human trafficking, call authorities when we observe something that looks suspicious, or volunteer in our communities.

1
FROM SILENCED TO SAVED

JENELLE GOODRICH

PART 1, SIERRA, FEBRUARY 2017

"Can you put your phone down?" Jenelle asked, but the girl didn't respond.

"Will you *please* put your phone down?" Jenelle repeated with a little more *umph*. The fourteen-year-old hadn't uttered one word for five minutes straight and refused to look up from her phone. Jenelle wasn't one to give up easily, so she pressed on, "Your parents brought you in here, so let's make use of this time. What do you say?"

The girl briefly raised her head away from her phone, rolled her eyes, and made an inaudible sound indicating that sitting with

Jenelle in the conference room was the last place in the world she wanted to be.

Thirty-year-old Jenelle Goodrich worked for the McDermott Center, which specialized in family counseling. She briefly looked out the small window and continued, "Look Sierra, I get it; you're angry, so let's talk about it. I want to get to know you," Jenelle coaxed, looking to motivate the girl, but she remained uncommunicative.

Jenelle slightly brushed her blonde hair behind her right ear and continued, "You don't want your parents hassling you anymore, do you?" Jenelle asked, trying once again to encourage Sierra to engage in conversation. Her first session with the teen wasn't going anywhere.

Sierra paused on her phone for a second, and slowly looked up and made eye contact. Her eyes were burning with hatred for Jenelle. Her mouth tightened up and she clenched her teeth.

"I don't want to talk to you, okay?" Sierra suddenly snapped loudly, the sound reverberating off the walls of the small conference room. "Don't you get it? This is a waste of my time!" She stared at Jenelle with complete contempt.

Jenelle didn't flinch. She expected a teen diagnosed with *oppositional defiant disorder* to be angry, irritable, and easily lose her temper. The typical teen is already moody, petulant, and argumentative, but those with ODD take it to the next level.

Sierra was a solid student, but this semester she racked up D's and F's with no obvious explanation. She wasn't skipping school, so that wasn't it. She was arguing more often with her parents and dropped the friends she'd known since middle school.

She cussed out her coach and was kicked off the Freshman volleyball team. Her parents were at their wits' end and didn't know what else to do, so the school guidance counselor recommended that the three of them attend family counseling.

It would have been so much easier to be a theology professor, Jenelle thought. She graduated last year from a small private Christian university with a degree in theology and a minor in philosophy and counseling. She wanted to be a professor, but job opportunities were thin in the Denver metro area, and they weren't any better nationwide.

The only job openings available required more experience and a master's degree. But how are you supposed to get experience if you can't land that initial job? *It seemed like the only time they were hiring was when an old tenured professor passed away.* McDermott placed an ad for a counselor\case manager and she was hired.

"I get it, you're angry," Jenelle stated calmly and then suggested, "Tell me what you're angry about." Sierra didn't answer and Jenelle stared at the teen sitting in the chair of the small room who was attempting to look busy and interested in her phone.

Sierra had long, dark hair with pink dyed tips and was of average height, about five feet two inches tall. Her skin was imperfect, as was common with teens of that age. She carried a few extra pounds, but nothing close to being overweight although she held her phone close to her waistline as if to cover it up.

Maybe she has body image issues, Jenelle thought to herself, *but then what teen girl doesn't?* On its own, low self-esteem isn't usually enough to make someone *this* angry, so maybe there's something deeper? Jenelle was gently pushing to get the teen's attention.

"How are your classes going this semester?" Jenelle asked, although she already knew the answer. She didn't want to come across with an accusatory tone that would cause the teen to immediately become defensive or shut down completely.

"My teachers suck," Sierra snarled without looking up.

"Can you put the phone down for a moment?" Jenelle asked softly. Sierra continued to type into her phone. Jenelle waited silently for a full minute, and then finally Sierra stopped and looked up at her but didn't say anything.

"It looks like your grade in math went from a 'B' to an 'F,' do you want some help from a tutor?"

"No, I don't need a stupid tutor," Sierra quipped in an obvious sarcastic tone and rolled her eyes in disgust.

"You had a decent grade in math. I know you aren't stupid, so did you stop studying?" Jenelle questioned.

"Who needs math anyway? It's a waste of my time," Sierra retorted.

"Is that why you stopped doing your homework?" Sierra ignored the question and picked up her phone and started texting someone.

"You probably hate school, right?" Jenelle inquired, looking for something that would prompt the teen to talk. Sierra stopped texting for the moment, rolled her eyes big time, and breathed a small sigh that communicated her thoughts, *Well duh, of course I hate school!*

"I know high school can be a drag, and all you want to do is hang out with your friends . . ."

"I don't have any friends," Sierra interrupted with a snotty tone and stared off into a corner of the room.

"Most people don't go from good grades to failing grades without something going on. I want to help you."

"Whatever," Sierra muttered under her breath.

"Why don't we talk about . . ." Jenelle suggested but was cut off.

"I already said that I don't want to be here," Sierra answered with a defiant tone and stood up. "Everybody is always on my case, whether it's you, my parents, or teachers. I'm sick of all of you.

I just want to be left alone. And school sucks. My so-called friends suck too, and I don't want to be in school. *Isn't that obvious*," Sierra sneered and walked out of the conference room without waiting for an answer.

Jenelle guessed the root of her behavior wasn't her struggle with grades because Sierra was clearly angry at something or someone. Maybe both.

32 DAYS LATER

Jenelle welcomed Sierra's parents into the small conference room. They seemed nice enough and provided a decent, middle-class home. Both were employed and Jenelle didn't detect any immediate red flags such as substance abuse or domestic violence. They looked like a nice couple whose only child was out of control.

"I'm guessing she's still defiant at home," Jenelle queried.

"Yes, she is. Nothing is going well, and Sierra has a problem with *everything*. She's failing most of her classes and we get into an argument every day," replied the exasperated woman. "They're *ugly* arguments. She knows how to push my buttons and we're immediately in a screaming match," Pam told her and let out a loud sigh.

"Yelling is only going to feed her defiance," Jenelle told her.

"Well, it sure seems that way and we never resolve anything. But it's so hard when your own daughter tells you that she hates you. I'm getting to the end of my rope, and I don't know what to do," the thirty-seven-year-old mom told Jenelle. She was desperate for answers while Sierra's father, Alan, nodded his head in silence.

"I am building some trust with her, but it's been a slow process. She has a new set of friends that I've been trying to get Sierra to open up about. Does she have a boyfriend?" Jenelle asked.

"I don't think so. She was never one of the popular girls," Pam chimed in, "but she had a small group of friends, some real nice girls." Her eyes slightly diverted to look at the ceiling as if in thought, and then continued, "but I haven't seen or heard anything about them in months."

"I brought that up the other day with Sierra since I haven't seen her friend Claire in a long time," Alan interjected. "She responded with her typical bad *attitude* and told me that Claire is stuck up and too good for her. I don't know what to make of that."

"Did she reveal anything specific?" Jenelle probed.

"No, she ran up to her room as usual," Alan answered. "She never gives any details, no matter how many questions I ask." *But then a clue came up.* "My wife tried calling Claire's mother but didn't get a whole lot of information either."

"Yeah," Pam explained, "Claire's mom told me that the girls hadn't been friends in several months, and Sierra started running around with a different, *rougher* crowd. She mentioned this other girl Myra, whom I had never heard of."

"Did Claire's mom know anything about this new friend?" Jenelle asked.

"No. I confronted Sierra about Myra, but she refused to talk about her, and we immediately got into another argument. Maybe I should have taken a gentler approach? I don't know," Pam wondered and shook her head with despair.

"No approach is working," Alan added.

Pam added, "The tender approach doesn't work with Sierra and neither does tough love. Anything and *everything* I say makes her angry." Defeated, Pam slumped in her chair and looked physically exhausted.

"Not to change the subject, but I guess there's something else you should know," Alan commented. Jenelle gave a slight nod and he continued, "I'm sure it's not helping the situation."

"What is it?" Jenelle inquired. Pam turned to stare at her husband with a sudden annoyed expression on her face.

"I don't think that's the problem," Pam cut in.

"What's going on?" Jenelle asked.

"Well Pam and I . . ." he trailed off and then sighed loudly. "My wife and I have not been getting along very well for the past year or so, and we recently decided to separate."

"Children pick up on that tension; there's no doubt about it," Jenelle told them.

"We don't fight in front of Sierra," Pam countered in a defensive tone.

"She still knows if something isn't right," Jenelle stated.

"Maybe she is trying to get back at us," Alan conceded.

"Possibly. A teen's reaction is complicated and inconsistent. She may be lashing out for attention; she may blame one or both of you," Jenelle replied.

"It seems to be more than just blame, she is *so very angry*," Alan replied.

"She may be angry with everyone, including herself, and that could explain her outbursts, bad grades, and sudden change in her friends' group. But it could be something more, and I haven't been able to put my finger on it," Jenelle stated in a calm manner.

"Please help my baby girl," Pam begged. "She's not only angry, but she also seems *so sad.* I know she's hurting, but I don't know how to help her," she apologized and wiped away a small tear from her left eye.

"I'm doing everything I can," Jenelle softly reassured her. I've got my individual session with Sierra starting in a few minutes, so will you two wait in the lobby?"

"Yes, we'll send her in," Alan said with a sigh and a depressed tone. He stood up and then added, "Come on, Pam."

A minute later, Sierra entered the small conference room. "So, how are you this afternoon?" asked Jenelle. Sierra shrugged her shoulders without saying a word and sat down. *Here we go again,* Jenelle thought.

"So, tell me about your friend Myra," Jenelle suggested. *No reason to waste any time with small talk.*

"How did you know about her?" Sierra shot back quickly with a surprised tone.

"She's your friend at school, right?"

"Kind of, but I still want to know how you found out about her."

"Myra must hang out with you and your new boyfriend," Jenelle stated, ignoring Sierra's request. She didn't know if Sierra had a boyfriend or not. But since she surprised Sierra about Myra, *and she was at least talking,* Jenelle attempted to bluff a question to penetrate a little deeper.

"You know about Rodrigo, too?"

Bingo, the bluff worked!

"Of course," Jenelle answered without skipping a beat, "You've been dating him for a little while, so what's he like?"

"He's cool, not like the other jerks at school. He's mature."

"How old is he?"

"I dunno."

"But he's older right? Guys in high school can be real losers. Boys at your age are *so immature*, aren't they?" Jenelle asked in jest, trying to find common ground with Sierra.

"Maybe he's twenty-one. He's got his own place," she answered with a wry smile, clearly trying to impress Jenelle. "He thinks I'm pretty hot."

"Wow, that's a real man you got there," Jenelle told her and raised her eyebrow, nodded her head, and slightly smiled, clearly indicating to Sierra that she had her attention.

And Sierra *definitely had Jenelle's attention now*, as her antenna went on full alert. Why is a twenty-one-year-old dating a fourteen-year-old? That would clearly be statutory rape if they were having sex. She needed to keep digging and wouldn't ignore the signs.

"Well, I hope you're using protection," Jenelle bluntly stated, never one to beat around the bush.

"I didn't say anything about *that*," Sierra returned with a small sheepish grin.

"Come on, a pretty girl like you with an older guy, it doesn't take a genius to figure out what's going on with your big romance."

"Yeah, I am popular with his friends, too," she reflexively answered and her facial expression immediately changed to indicate disgust, and then gasped when she realized what she'd let out.

"What do you mean?"

"Nothing," Sierra snarled with sudden building anger.

"Do you party with his friends?" Jenelle asked.

"I don't want to talk about it," Sierra answered and then immediately shut down. She slightly bit her lower lip, and Jenelle could see the wheels turning in her head. Sierra expressed a solemn look that morphed into more anger.

"Stop bugging me!" Sierra snapped with a raised voice, "I'm done talking to you," and reverted to looking at her phone refusing to say a word for the rest of their session.

1 DAY LATER

"I took some of those screenshots from Myra and Sierra's social media posts," Officer Jesse Barnes stated. "Sierra hasn't been active lately, but they both had pictures with this one particular guy."

"Let me guess, his name is Rodrigo?" Jenelle inquired sarcastically.

"You got it," the officer answered. "He's *twenty-nine years old* and has a rap sheet that includes assault, drug possession, and the one you'll be interested in, sexual exploitation of a minor."

"Can you build a case against this guy for statutory rape?"

"Yes, I've already opened up a file, but I think it's worse than that."

"What do you mean?"

"Although there's been no arrests, he's on our watch list for distribution of child pornography."

"Oh no, what has this girl gotten herself into?"

"That's what we're trying to find out. When are you talking to her next?"

"In a couple days."

"Good. See if you can get some more details. There are many child pornography and underage 'escort' websites on the dark web, so it'd be helpful if you can get something that'll point us in the right direction."

"I'll let you know as soon as I talk to her on Monday," Jenelle replied. She had a sick feeling in her gut. She could immediately feel the acid grinding and churning and for a moment she thought she might throw up. Just the thought of this fourteen-year-old girl being exploited repulsed her beyond belief. She knew that these crimes existed, but when she took the job as a counselor and case manager, she had no idea that one of her first clients could be exploited so viciously.

4 DAYS LATER

"Can we talk about Rodrigo?" Jenelle asked in a gentle manner. Sierra sat in the conference room clearly not in the mood for conversation. She was already agitated.

"Sierra, I want to help you. I care about what happens to you, and I don't want to see you get hurt anymore. Do you know that Rodrigo's actually twenty-nine years old?"

"I don't believe you, and who says I've been hurt?" Sierra answered, attempting to be confident, and folded her arms. "He loves me," she said in his defense, but no one was buying that argument.

"What about Rodrigo taking pictures of you and the movies?" Jenelle directly asked with confidence but was actually probing for information.

"What? How did you find out *about that*?" Sierra gasped, horrified that Jenelle might have seen the videos. "He says I have a sexy look and can be a model," she added, trying to divert the discussion away from the content of the video. She involuntarily started to squirm in her seat.

"Tell me what happened."

"It's no big deal," she claimed.

"You know it is," Jenelle countered.

"I love him and I know he loves me," she stated unconvincingly.

"How do you know?"

"I just do," she said with some dissipating defiance. Her strong wall was starting to crack.

"Was he your first?" Jenelle asked.

"Yeah," she admitted after a long pause and then added, "he told me *that* made him love me even more," she appealed with little persuasion.

"Tell me about the photoshoot sessions," Jenelle suggested, wanting to move along the conversation.

"Well, it started out with a few sexy poses. He convinced me that I could model for *Victoria's Secret*."

Not at fourteen, Jenelle thought to herself, but said nothing, then asked, "But he wanted photos with less and less clothes?"

"How did you know?" Sierra asked. "He told me that it would help him pay rent and help his business," Sierra attempted to explain.

"Sweetie, this *is a big deal*. I know you think you're almost grown up and mature, but you're fourteen years old and you've gotten in way too deep with this guy. Is he also making you have sex on camera?"

"He begged me to help him make money. He said he'd be evicted otherwise. I didn't really want to . . ." Sierra trailed off, reliving what had happened.

"All on his iPhone? Other guys, too?"

Sierra nodded. "It happened several times with some of his friends," she admitted without making eye contact.

"Does he make movies for a living?" Jenelle asked. *This is worse than I thought.*

"I dunno, I guess. He's the only one that understands me, and I wanted to show him *how much I love him*," Sierra answered and started to cry. She was slightly shaking and was clearly conflicted about how much she wanted to reveal to Jenelle. Her lips trembled and her face was contorted with pain from the inner conflict coming to the surface. Jenelle waited patiently in silence to give her a moment.

"He told me I was the prettiest girlfriend he's ever had; no one ever said that to me before," Sierra remarked in a poor attempt to defend Rodrigo and continued, "He told me it would only be one time, but . . ." she remarked and trailed off.

"But it wasn't just once, was it?" Jenelle asked.

"It happened a couple of times. He was *so proud of me*. He said that he was going to make a lot of coin," Sierra answered and then completely broke down. She cried and Jenelle quietly handed her a box of tissues.

"I'm so sorry, honey, but you know that isn't true love. No one deserves to be treated like that."

"Yeah, I guess. But ever since I got in trouble at school, my parents never let me out of their sight. I haven't seen him in a long time. I miss my boyfriend."

"I know you are in pain," Jenelle said in a comforting manner and handed her another tissue.

"Then he made me watch the video," Sierra whispered in shame and continued, "It was disgusting! I have no idea who the other guy was," she cringed and buried her face in her hands and cried uncontrollably. Her makeup smeared, and the running black eyeliner gave her face a ghoulish tone.

Jenelle herself teared up from hearing about Sierra's ordeal and gladly gave Sierra a few minutes to try to compose herself.

"He'd show me these porn videos and told me I had to do the same things," Sierra moaned while sobbing and then blurted out, "And he was going to send the video to my parents if I didn't keep doing what he said!"

"He was blackmailing you and forcing you into having sex with him and others. That is horrible; what he did to you is completely illegal."

"It is? I didn't try to stop him," Sierra commented.

"That doesn't matter. It's very much illegal and he committed multiple felonies."

"Yeah, but most times it wasn't recorded, just me there to do *whatever* his friends wanted," Sierra admitted and continued, "They would come into the bedroom one after the other for hours. Afterwards, he'd flash a wad of cash."

"You were coerced and exploited, and I am going to help you out of this situation. We'll need to go to the police." Jenelle concluded with both compassion and steely resolve.

"He was the love of my life; I thought we'd be together forever," Sierra gulped with despair and blew her nose.

Jenelle was angry and vowed to herself to stop this evil. She breathed slowly to calm herself and then offered, "We're going to stop this from happening again, okay?"

"Okay," Sierra answered softly and then added, "It's like we broke up without ever saying those words. It just hurts."

"He's manipulated you; I hope you can see that."

"I know," she admitted and then added, "Myra was doing the same thing." Jenelle guessed that Sierra was desperately clinging to the notion that if she wasn't the only one, it would somehow make it better. Tears streamed down her face and she was visibly distraught.

With Myra involved too, Jenelle knew that Officer Jesse Barnes was going to have a lot to investigate.

Jenelle was about to comment, but Sierra spoke first, "You can't tell my parents, okay? Rodrigo will kill them."

"What do you mean?"

"Somehow, he made a copy of my house key. He always had it in his pocket and he'd take it out and show me. He told me he could come into my house at any time to kill me or my parents. What was I supposed to do?"

Jenelle took a deep breath to compose herself again and said, "Look at me. You were exploited in the cruelest way, but I am going to help you. I want to ask you something, and it's really, really important, so I need you to concentrate."

"What is it?" Sierra asked.

"Think about Rodrigo talking to his friends or anyone else for that matter. Did he ever mention a website he might upload the pictures and videos to? Or maybe a name of a company?" Jenelle calmly appealed and gently held Sierra's hands.

Sierra continued to cry for almost another minute as she played the horrors over in her mind. Jenelle patiently waited to see if she could answer.

Sierra was still looking down at her hands and wouldn't make eye contact with Jenelle, and then told her in a soft tone, "I heard something about *Sweaty Pig Productions*. I remembered that name because I thought I learned something in school that in fact, pigs don't sweat."

LATER THAT EVENING

"I feel it in my gut–I have to help this girl," Jenelle stated to her husband Casey while pacing in the living room. She had to do something with her excess nervous energy.

"I can't imagine what this girl is going through," he responded.

"It's more than this one girl. My supervisor wants me to take on more clients like this," Jenelle commented, and would change names and details when talking to her husband or anyone else.

"Really? I thought you wanted to stick to family counseling," he replied and slowly stroked his lumberjack-style beard.

"I know, I said I didn't want to have any clients with sex crimes or pornography addiction. I still feel that way, but I'm being pulled in this direction. I can't explain it, but there's a feeling deep inside that I must be there for these girls. I guess you could say that *I am compelled*."

"I get it; if that's what you want to do, I'll support you. But it's going to be a very difficult job."

"Yeah, I know this is not going to be some cushy nine-to-five office job," Jenelle answered in an exasperated tone.

"I can tell you care about your clients. You've got a big heart," Casey commented.

"I've been doing a little research, and human trafficking takes many different forms and is happening everywhere. You think you live in a nice suburban town outside of Denver, but it's happening right under our noses."

"You mean someone who's been kidnapped?" Casey asked.

"That's actually pretty rare. Many are runaways. And one third are lured into sex trafficking within the first forty-eight hours of being on the street. That's hundreds of thousands of kids in this country alone. Most of the activity isn't on the border–it's here in the suburbs."

"Wow, that's a ton of kids," Casey said.

"And it is not only runaways, but they can be deceived by a family member, someone in a foster home, or school friends, like the case I'm working now. This girl got in with the wrong crowd and was given attention and compliments by an older boyfriend. He got his hooks into her, manipulating her into sex trafficking, which can include child pornography. I had no idea that it could happen to suburban high school kids."

"That surprises me too, and it's so disgusting," Casey cringed.

"The internet has done a lot of great things, but this is a huge negative fallout, where people from all over the world can access websites with child porn on it, and it's a significant money-making business."

"Yeah, I heard human trafficking makes more money than the NFL, NBA, and MLB combined," Casey stated.

"And forced prostitution is even more lucrative than the drug business," Jenelle pointed out.

"What do you mean?"

"Well, if you are a drug dealer or run a meth house, you have to keep creating and selling more product, but with forced prostitution, you can use the same girl over and over again. And that's exactly what it is; *she's been used.* There's little cost and it's easier to avoid detection from law enforcement compared to drug dealing. Some of these pimps make three hundred thousand per year from one young girl."

"The world is dark, and it makes me so angry that men purchase kids."

"It's crazy. The only business that made more money than human trafficking was Apple Computer."

"That's a shitload," Casey recoiled.

"Yes, and it's happening right here in our own city. Officer Barnes told me that each year, they work on cases that involve about a hundred girls and boys being trafficked. But he estimates that there's a thousand more like them," Jenelle said, and the seriousness sunk in after she spoke.

"That's an overwhelming number," Casey commented and scrunched his brow, trying to make sense of all the information. He shifted the stance of his solid frame and spoke, "And Denver isn't one of the largest cities in the country. It has to be worse in places like Los Angeles and New York."

"Yeah, and they are hiding in plain sight," Jenelle answered.

"You've done your homework on this."

"I have, and I talked to someone at St. Abbo's church in Aurora. I've decided to volunteer there, running a faith-based trauma-informed group for human trafficking victims and survivors."

"That sounds intense," Casey added before pausing a moment, "Are there that many local girls to fill an entire class?"

"Yes, there are about a dozen girls, and a few boys too. I'm not sure what I'm getting into," Jenelle stammered with a nervous laugh.

"You're going to be great. Those kids will be lucky to have you," Casey said and took a step towards his wife and put his hands on her arms.

"Thanks," Jenelle commented and then softly said, "They don't leave my mind when they leave the room."

27 DAYS LATER

"I'm so tired," Jenelle stated with a loud sigh a few seconds after entering the house.

"What's going on?" Casey asked.

"I love these girls, I really do, but sometimes I get so frustrated."

"With them?"

"Well yes," she smiled and laughed and then continued, "But I was referring to the system. Whether it's the foster system, the criminal justice system, or the way many nonprofits are run. There's a lot of bureaucracy and protocols."

"Well, it's the government, so what did you expect? But what exactly do you mean?"

"Each one of these cases is so unique; it doesn't fit in a neat little box on a government form. It's chaotic, and it changes every day!" Jenelle explained, and Casey nodded in agreement.

"My job at the counseling center isn't much better; they're obviously trying to run a business," Jenelle stated, talking a mile a minute, "but I can't charge extra money if these girls contact me outside of our sessions, which happens all the time."

"Who would be stupid enough to think they'd only need you when you're in the office?" Casey asked.

"I'm going to take those phone calls or texts. Most of the crap that happens to them is after five p.m., which is outside of normal business hours. I want the freedom to work with them when it's necessary, and not be constrained by organizational bureaucracy," Jenelle said in an infuriated tone.

"I understand wanting to avoid bureaucracy," Casey agreed, as someone who appreciated running his own business.

"Many of these nonprofits are more interested in their next round of grants rather than what's best for these kids. I understand that they need an inflow of money, but it's frustrating when the kids that need their help aren't their number one priority."

"This is why you do this and not me. I'd get so upset and start yelling at these idiots," Casey replied. Jenelle nodded with understanding.

"Do you know what one organization told me?" Jenelle asked but didn't wait for an answer, "They told me not to answer a text or phone call from one of my clients."

"They sound like morons."

"I completely agree, but it's because contact outside of a counseling session could later result in legal liability issues."

"What?" Casey responded with surprise.

"Yeah, they expect me to ignore them if it's communication outside of the office. How am I supposed to do that when these girls are in crisis? *How could I do that to my clients?*"

"That's not how you operate," Casey concluded with the authority of knowing his wife for over a decade.

"That's why I'm thinking of going out on my own," she said and continued, "I can't sit here and deal with all of this red tape."

"You want to do counseling on your own?"

"No, I mean doing more case management. Figuring out what the situation is and immediately getting these girls what's needed and setting them up with the right people or the right agency that can help them. That's a lot more hands-on than many counselors or nonprofits want to get."

"That's going to give these girls or boys the most meaningful assistance," Casey concluded.

"Exactly, which is why I'm thinking of setting up my own nonprofit. I want to guide them from their current situation to something stable, secure, *and safe.*"

"That's a big decision; I've got your back," Casey told her.

"I don't like it, but it's clearly what's being put in my path. I'm overwhelmed *every single day*, but God has smacked me in the back of the head and is telling me to go in that direction. These kids are human; they have value and they're worth it. I can't ignore it."

"How can I help?"

"Just being here and letting me ramble on . . ." she answered and smiled.

"You aren't rambling," he responded in a serious tone.

"Thanks. After my mom died, I remember my dad once told me that God trusts His best soldiers with solving the biggest problems because He knows they can handle it. I looked at him like he was insane. I didn't want God trusting me so much."

"Well, He does."

"I know, but I'm so tired at the end of the day. Sometimes, I simply want a normal office job. Why couldn't I have been an accountant?"

"That's not you," Casey said with a chuckle and smiled. They both knew that was the truth.

* * *

You are not hidden
There's never been a moment
You were forgotten
You are not hopeless
Though you have been broken
Your innocence stolen
There is no distance
That cannot be covered
Over and over
You're not defenseless
I'll be your shelter
I'll be your armor
"Rescue" - Lauren Daigle

25 DAYS LATER, MAY 2017

Jenelle was pleased with the progress she'd made with Sierra, who had no further contact with Rodrigo. When Jenelle followed up with Officer Barnes, he confirmed that they had a solid case against Rodrigo and several of his associates. They were getting close to making an arrest and could move forward without any testimony from Sierra, but obviously, her assistance would help tremendously.

Jenelle brought in Officer Barnes to break the news to her parents. This upset Sierra and she missed several scheduled appointments with Jenelle. In the first session when she returned, she yelled for eight minutes straight. The venting helped get some of the anger out of her system. Sierra was embarrassed that anyone knew about her situation and continued hurting greatly. She wanted to forget the whole thing, but deep down she understood that wasn't possible.

Alan and Pam could not believe that their daughter was mixed up with sex trafficking. It was even worse than they imagined after they learned that Rodrigo videoed her performing sexual acts, although that would be key evidence in the criminal case.

Alan and Pam were also going through emotional turmoil, and it was easier for them to remain in a state of denial. That method of coping changed the day they saw a strange car parked near their house. It was Rodrigo, and they suspected he wanted to find Sierra and lure her back into the life, and probably by force.

"In the life" is a term used when a trafficking victim is being actively exploited. Sierra's parents called the police and when a patrol car showed up, Rodrigo immediately drove away. It was obvious he was trying to get his claws back into Sierra. That day, they changed the locks to their home.

From that moment on, Alan and Pam never let their daughter out of their sight, and they put their divorce plans on hold. Sierra was lucky in that respect because that gave her a better chance to be a survivor. One of them would bring Sierra to school, walking her to the door, and would be there as soon as school let out. They didn't need to convince Sierra to stay in the house since she immediately ran up to her room and cried. *And kept crying.* She cried for hours until her eyes were red and puffy, with the energy drained from her body and mind.

Sierra remained resentful that Jenelle brought in the police and other authorities. Jenelle was pleased when she received a call that Sierra wanted to continue her counseling. As angry as Sierra was, Jenelle hoped that Sierra was ready to begin the healing process. As painful as it was, Sierra was relieved that it had been exposed and that she was out of the life.

"I didn't want to do it, but I let Rodrigo tell me what to do," Sierra confessed.

"You're the victim, Sierra; Rodrigo took advantage of you and committed so many crimes."

"But I didn't fight them off. I don't want to *be a victim*," Sierra stated. She wanted to pretend that it was all a bad dream.

"You were manipulated. You're fourteen. He's twenty-nine and saw you as vulnerable. He was targeting you from the first day he saw you. You were simply a way to make him money. Emphasis on *were*."

"I can't believe I loved him," Sierra exclaimed and shook her head, wiping a tear from her eye.

"He'd say anything to convince you he was a great boyfriend. Guys like him are master manipulators, and over time you'll see that."

"Yeah, and he never treated me like a real girlfriend. We never went out on dates and he never introduced me as his girlfriend to anyone else. I should have known better . . ." she observed and trailed off.

"You can't blame yourself. If you get one thing from our talks, please believe it when I say, it was not your fault," Jenelle told her.

"Okay," she answered but with little conviction.

Jenelle expected Sierra's state of mind because the healing process was slow and never flipped like a switch. "And another thing, you are no longer a victim; you're now a *survivor*. There is another life after this and that's what you need to focus on," Jenelle told her with the confidence of an expert. "You can count on me until you get your strength back."

"Okay," Sierra answered, still not convinced, but needed to hear the words.

"You're going to have a wide variety of feelings about this and you're going to struggle over a long period of time, maybe your whole life," Jenelle told her, not sugarcoating Sierra's situation.

Sierra nodded and continued to look down.

"Honestly, you're going to feel crappy a lot of the time, and it's normal to have your emotions all over the place. There will be a lot of work and unfortunately, it isn't going to go away overnight. But you have your whole life ahead of you and you can get to the other side of this."

"Yeah, I get so angry sometimes. At Rodrigo, at myself, at my parents, at my friends, and especially Myra. She *knew* what Rodrigo was going to do to me *and she recruited me anyway!*"

"That's how it happens sometimes, another girl who seems safe will befriend someone for the sole purpose of exploiting her."

"How could she do this to me? How could I be so stupid?" Sierra burst out wailing. She was in deep pain, reliving the last few months.

"Officer Barnes told me that no one can find Myra," Jenelle added.

"Yeah, I haven't seen her in over a month," Sierra responded, and the implication was ominous.

"Hopefully, the police will find her." Jenelle wanted to get back on point and continued, "You're going to get through this, you're going to be able to get back *your* life; I know you can do this."

It was a long and usually unsuccessful process to move someone from victim to survivor, but that was exactly what Jenelle strived for these kids. She didn't want them to view themselves as a victim their whole lives. She wanted them to live as a survivor. Jenelle's goal in life was for these girls to live a *normal and very boring life*.

"Why did God allow Rodrigo to do such awful things to me?" Sierra asked and looked up at Jenelle.

Jenelle was a little surprised that she brought up the subject of religion. Sierra didn't grow up in a household with any religious or faith foundation. *So, why would she ask me this question now? Faith and trust in God usually didn't resonate with girls like Sierra.*

Jenelle had been fielding that question ever since she started working with the girls and boys who'd been trafficked.

"Sierra, it would be so easy if only bad things happen to bad people and good things happened to good people. But that's not how it works. Since the beginning of time, there's been evil in the world, and unfortunately, that's the only way I can categorize Rodrigo."

"But why did this happen *to me*? What did I do to deserve this?" she asked and started tearing up again.

"You didn't do *anything* to deserve this."

Sierra sat silently.

"I'll give it to you straight: people have free will and there's evil in the heart of some humans and a lust for the flesh. If everything were perfect, then we wouldn't have room to grow," Jenelle explained.

Sierra was still looking down, but she was listening intently, so Jenelle spoke again, "God doesn't orchestrate evil, but He does use all things for the betterment in the future, and we just can't see it yet. God loves you, Sierra, as a specific individual," Jenelle stated, and the teen slightly looked up but did not make eye contact.

"Yeah, I guess," Sierra softly whispered.

"A doctor can help heal your hurt body, but only God can help the injured soul." Jenelle wanted to tell her so much more, but she knew that Sierra probably would be pushed away from God if she pressed too hard. She knew that it wasn't her place to impose religion on this very traumatized teen. Jenelle's tactic was to show Sierra her own love and servitude of Christ, not to convert Sierra.

5 DAYS LATER

"Well, I've made my final decision. I'm going to quit my job and start the nonprofit," Jenelle told her sister.

"You've been talking about this for a while," Jordan replied.

"Yes, I'm all in. I'm going to tell my manager later today."

"That's awesome. You're going to impact so many lives, help so many people, and you're going to be great at it."

"I'm about to make the jump, but I have to tell you, I am a little scared. Can I really do it? Am I the right person to help these girls?"

"You can. Your life and career will be forever changed, so it's only normal to have some doubts," Jordan answered in a reassuring tone.

"They have many different needs. Each one is different, and I will have to navigate that. It should be comprehensive. I need to be more than a mentor or counselor who meets with them once a week. Every fiber of my being is telling me to do this," Jenelle told her.

"Then you've made the right decision," Jordan concluded.

"Now I need to figure out a name. I'm thinking of *the Denver Hope Project*, but I'm not thrilled with it. I don't know; I'm not excited about any of the names I've come up with. I've got to figure that out."

After a few seconds, Jordan suggested, "How about *From Silenced to Saved*?"

"Hmmm," Jenelle paused and then it struck her. "Hey, Jordan, that's pretty good."

"These kids were silenced by their tormentor. Society let them down and they felt as if no one cared. They didn't have their freedom and couldn't talk about what was happening to them. And you're trying to help them become a survivor, where they are saved from being trafficked," Jordan added.

"I like it."

"Maybe they will eventually be saved with the love of Jesus."

"Hopefully. Jordan, that's a great name. It's more than great; I think it's perfect."

"Cool. Your life will never be the same after this."

"I know, and I'm nervous about taking this step, and there's a part of me that doubts that I can do this, but I feel like it's a calling. It's in my gut and in my heart."

"Mom would be proud," Jordan beamed.

198 DAYS LATER, NOVEMBER 2017

"Watermelon Berry is my favorite," Sierra volunteered with enthusiasm.

"That's a good one," Jenelle added and noticed that Sierra was actually smiling. The two of them sat at a small table at the Nekter Juice Bar. "Thanks for buying these," Jenelle said and took a sip of her smoothie, "You didn't have to do that."

"You're welcome; I've got some money thanks to this babysitting job I started a few weeks ago. It keeps me busy."

"Who are you babysitting?"

"A neighbor kid that I watch after school until one of her parents comes home. She's in the third grade and sometimes I help her with her homework," Sierra commented.

"That's great; speaking of homework, how are your grades coming along?" Jenelle inquired.

"Definitely better, I'm getting mostly 'Bs' this semester."

"That's pretty good."

"Yeah, but I will have to go to summer school again to make up some credits."

"That will put you back on track before you're in the eleventh grade. Are you going to all your counseling sessions?"

"Yes, the person you set me up with is helping. I still have my rough days, but the counselor is keeping me focused. Well, most of the time," Sierra joked.

"It's hard, but compared to where you were a few months ago, life is so much better," Jenelle observed.

"I know I have to keep going."

"It's been over a month since we got together. Is there anything you want to talk about specifically?" Jenelle asked.

"Not really, I'm just getting through each day," Sierra answered, pushed her dangling hair behind her ears, and continued, "Some days are harder than others, but I am trying to focus on my schoolwork."

"I am happy you're getting your life back."

"Officer Barnes told me that they haven't been able to find Rodrigo, and they suspect he's on the run and left the area," Sierra relayed.

"He told me the same thing. Hopefully, Rodrigo will make a mistake, and they'll arrest him," Jenelle offered.

"It's a little scary knowing that Rodrigo is still out there. I get stressed out worrying that I might run into him someday."

"It's not likely, but it is possible, so you'll have to have your guard up and be aware of your surroundings. If you see him, you start screaming at the top of your lungs no matter where you are."

"I will try," Sierra promised. "Being here with you is one of the few times that I'm not under the watchful eye of a teacher or my parents."

"They want to keep you safe," Jenelle reminded her.

"I know, I know."

"How are you getting along with your parents?"

"Things are better, that's for sure. But they want to know where I am every second, which I understand," Sierra commented.

"They obviously love you. You're lucky because that isn't always the case," Jenelle told her, and Sierra nodded her head in understanding.

"After everything that's happened, I don't blame them. As much as I want more freedom, I guess it keeps me out of trouble."

"Are they continuing with marriage counseling?"

"Yes, so maybe that will help them," Sierra said with a hopeful tone.

"They're trying, so there's a reason to be optimistic."

"They're not fighting, and that's a start, I suppose," Sierra stated, letting out a long and loud sigh.

"What is it?" Jenelle asked.

"Some days, I want to forget everything, but then out of nowhere, I will see or hear something that reminds me of what happened and I get an overwhelming feeling of panic," Sierra told her and looked down at her smoothie.

"A lot of bad things happened to you, so that reaction is normal, and it may never go away completely, but hopefully over time, it will happen less and less. You've made great progress, and I'm so proud of you."

"Thanks," Sierra said and produced a small smile on her face but didn't look up. "Although I don't feel like I've come that far."

"You're a survivor now. Trust me, there are a lot of kids in your situation that never make it this far. You should be proud of yourself and you can make even more progress," Jenelle appealed and then stressed, "Just work hard, stay focused and strong."

"I'll try."

"I know you can do it; I have faith in you and you know I'm just a text away," Jenelle reminded gently and held Sierra's hand. "If you need to talk to me about anything you know you can contact me anytime, right?"

"I know, thanks. I don't know how I could have made it this far without you."

PART 2, KIYRA AND SHANICE, DECEMBER 13, 2017

Jenelle was blissful and content. She retired early and fell asleep within minutes of her head hitting the pillow. This was a supreme luxury in a house with a husband and two kids and a job where client communication could occur at any time of the day or night. But on this rare evening, she slept uninterrupted and woke up refreshed.

She strolled downstairs to make a robust cup of French roast coffee and gazed at the clock, which told her it was 6:12 a.m. She impatiently waited for the last few drops to fall into the coffee pot.

She poured herself a cup of heaven. Steam rose from the *#1 Mom* mug she'd received for Mother's Day a few years ago and just before taking a sip, she inhaled the blissful scent from her fresh brew.

Jenelle reflected on how the time flew by since going out on her own. *Don't blink.* She was amazed that her life was *even busier*, and she gave herself a little mental pat on the back for keeping it all together, at least most of the time. It helped that Jenelle started using a color-coded daily planner book that kept her life organized and straight.

She took another sip of her delicious beverage, and just enjoyed the silence for a moment. She noticed the hum from the refrigerator, and then a neighbor's car off in the distance as it drove away. She felt tranquil and relaxed, enjoying her alone time. Her kids and husband were great, but sometimes she simply needed a little quiet time to recharge her batteries.

She noticed only one business appointment on her calendar, meeting for coffee with a new client, a fifteen-year-old sex trafficking victim. They would be joined by Dottie, a new volunteer she'd met a week ago after making a presentation at a church, discussing the facts of human trafficking in suburban America.

9 HOURS LATER

"I wanted to meet with you early, before Kiyra gets here. I'm excited about having you start as a volunteer," Jenelle said after they settled into a booth at the coffee shop.

"Me too. After I heard your talk at our church, I wanted to help these teens," Dottie replied in a bubbly tone. "The kids you talked about are the same age as my granddaughter."

"It surprises many people that the average age of someone forced into sex trafficking is about thirteen."

"Kiyra is fifteen now, right?" inquired the sixty-seven-year-old retiree.

"Yes. Officer Barnes referred her to me a few weeks ago, and I'm getting her set up with counseling. She spent some time in the juvenile detention center, and now she's with a new foster family. But she is at risk to be a runaway again."

"How do you mean?"

"She was in juvey when she was twelve for multiple shoplifting charges, and when she was with her third or fourth foster family in Greeley, she ran away again."

"Why did she run away?" Dottie asked.

"That's what this girl does; she runs. The family had four other foster kids in the house, and they seemed more interested in collecting a check than trying to help Kiyra. She got in an argument with an older foster sibling and was beat up."

"Is that common?" inquired Dottie.

"Yes, fighting among foster kids happens all the time. Kiyra escaped the situation by running away," Jenelle explained and continued, "The foster parents didn't report her missing for eleven days! So, by the time the police were contacted, she was nowhere to be found. Some of these foster families barely provide any care and support," she concluded with frustration.

"What happened after she ran away?"

"She was thirteen, living on the streets, and was immediately scooped up by one of the local gangs. Within two days, the gang had forced her into prostitution."

"Oh my, that's horrible!" Dottie exclaimed with disdain and shock. *It was no shock to Jenelle, unfortunately.*

"Yes, a sex slave at thirteen," Jenelle cringed and curled her lip in disgust and continued, "The gang members were also drug dealers and they used her as a mule."

"A mule?" Dottie asked.

"They made Kiyra transport the drugs between the buyer and seller. They do that so if someone is busted during the delivery, that someone is Kiyra instead of the gang member. Luckily for Kiyra, she was arrested."

"Lucky?"

"Yes, the buyer was an undercover police officer, and after she was arrested, they determined she was a runaway. She refused to go back to her old foster family, and they had nowhere to put her, so she was placed in juvey for a couple of weeks until they found a new foster family."

"Hopefully she's with a nice family," Dottie suggested.

"Maybe," Jenelle scoffed, having seen too many foster family situations a total mess, "They relocated her from Greely to Wheat Ridge."

"Is that when they contacted you?"

"Yes. These criminals enslaved her for over a year and a half," Jenelle replied.

"I can't imagine that."

"Especially at such a young age. When they first snatched her off the streets, the gang auctioned off her virginity to the highest bidder. Afterwards, she was gang-raped multiple times to break her spirit. It doesn't take long to break a thirteen-year-old."

"How does a girl survive that?" Dottie asked, fascinated.

"Obviously she's experienced so much trauma, and her recovery will take a long time. I'll help set her up with the right social services available. Today, I want to find out more about her current foster family."

"I hope she doesn't run away again."

"Me too; she needs stability and guidance," Jenelle agreed. "Assuming all goes well with her today, you'll be able to meet with Kiyra on your own."

"I'd like that," Dottie answered.

"We can talk afterwards about the dos and don'ts when it is just the two of you getting together. For today, I won't push her too hard, so just follow my lead in the conversation," Jenelle instructed.

"Of course," Dottie answered, "I want to be helpful. I've told all my friends about this, so maybe they'll also want to volunteer for your nonprofit. I am looking forward to meeting her."

"There she is," Jenelle said and waved across the room when she saw Kiyra.

2 DAYS LATER, DECEMBER 15, 2017

I am the road warrior and the car is my office, Jenelle thought to herself. Officer Barnes referred Shanice to Jenelle ten days ago. Shanice was recently charged and released with assaulting a security woman when she threw several bottles of perfume at Macy's. Officer Barnes suspected that she was involved in human trafficking but didn't have any evidence to move forward. Shanice refused to talk about it, but at least her name was now in the system. After several attempts to get in contact with her, Shanice finally agreed to meet up with Jenelle at a mall parking lot.

Jenelle easily spotted her and got out of her car. Shanice was wearing a provocative miniskirt, even though it was thirty-eight degrees outside, and she was walking slowly and seductively in her red shoes. She wore a tight sweater that hung off her shoulder, revealing her sixteen-year-old smooth ebony skin. It wasn't obvious how she arrived at the mall since she wasn't coming from the direction of the bus stop.

"Hi Shanice," she greeted her. "I'm Jenelle."

"Yeah, I'm here, so whatever," Shanice replied with a slight slur.

"There's a coffee shop over there where we can go and talk," she suggested, and when Shanice nodded, Jenelle turned to her left and started to walk. *That's when Shanice made her move.*

She pushed at Jenelle's shoulders, smashing her into the car, and lunged for Jenelle's large purse hanging from her shoulder. Shanice hooked her arm around the purse and tugged back. But out of habit, Jenelle always kept her hand firmly secured to the purse strap, and when Shanice yanked the purse, Jenelle followed and tumbled towards Shanice and fell down. However, she still held on to the purse and her momentum towards the ground forced Shanice to let go.

"What the hell?" Jenelle cried with surprise and quickly stood up. Just then, she heard tires screech from the other side of the parking lot. The man driving the car headed away from them. The easy robbery was a failure.

"Is he with you?" accused Jenelle.

"Maybe, so what?"

"What the hell is wrong with you?"

"With me?" Shanice sneered.

"You're the one who tried to rob me."

"Why not? You must have something good in there," Shanice replied with sarcasm, and Jenelle then noticed that Shanice didn't have any purse.

"I'm not going to cower like a scared little flower," Jenelle clapped back.

"Whatever, I thought you'd be an easy target, ya know, just some dumb white bitch," Shanice taunted and projected a menacing look.

Jenelle stood her ground, but calmly affirmed, "I came here to help you get out of the life. We can still talk," she suggested.

"I don't think so," Shanice retorted with a sarcastic tone, walked away, and started to text on her phone. The incident had started and finished in less than four minutes.

THAT EVENING

"How are you?"

"I'm fine," Jenelle answered which indicated more annoyance about the attempted robbery rather than any concern for her own safety.

"Are you sure?" Casey asked.

"Yes, it was a poor attempt at stealing my purse. I was a little shaken up afterwards knowing that if this girl's pimp got out of the car and they double-teamed me, the outcome may not have been so good," Jenelle said.

"Well, I'm glad you met in a public place; you need to be careful, especially if it's someone new. She could've had a weapon," Casey warned with a serious look on his face. "You always need to be cautious with new clients."

"Yep, I know," Jenelle acknowledged, fully aware that the situation could have easily and quickly become more dangerous.

"They expected you to be an easy target."

"Luckily, I was tougher than she thought and Shanice easily gave up."

"You seem pretty wound up."

"Yeah, but it's not just the robbery. I talked to this girl for only a few minutes. I tried texting her back, but she won't *or can't* answer," Jenelle told with a defeated tone. "I never had the chance to help her. I keep going over it in my mind, but there isn't anything I could have done differently."

"It all happened so fast, so what else could you have done?" Casey asked.

"I know, but it is more than that. Sometimes, it's just difficult to turn everything off."

"What you do is intense, so I'm not surprised that it's hard to stop thinking about it."

"It is what it is," she surmised and continued, "I struggle every day, and sometimes it seems like I'm running around like a chicken with her head cut off," she laughed in jest.

"Yes, I can see that!" Casey agreed with a chuckle that helped lighten the mood.

"Every day is a challenge, and most times, I don't make any

progress with these girls. They're always in crisis so there's little room for celebration. But every now and then, like the other day (with Sierra), I'll have a conversation with one of them and we're just talking about normal stuff."

"That's a successful day, isn't it?" Casey asked, returning to the seriousness of Jenelle's work.

"Yes, I know it sounds funny describing typical teenage activities as a huge success, but it's what we're *not talking about*."

"All the shit they're dealing with."

"Exactly! It's a good day when they aren't overwhelmed with the trauma of being trafficked, of getting raped, trying to kick drugs and alcohol, or having someone beat the crap out of them. If we're not dealing with any of that stuff, I call that a *pretty damn good day*," Jenelle asserted with an *oomph*.

"It's so much different from the average teenager's struggles."

"I'll take normal teenage drama any day," Jenelle said. "It's hard, but I love what I do and I'll keep moving forward."

"They may be small, but you have to take some of these successes as they come," Casey said.

"True. Also, I'm learning to do a better job of listening to the girls. It is not helpful if I'm doing all the talking."

"That's got to be hard for you, right?" he teased, knowing Jenelle was not one to keep quiet for very long.

"Yeah, you know me too well," she snickered.

3 DAYS LATER, DECEMBER 18, 2017

"Who was that old windbag?"

"What do you mean? What happened?" Jenelle returned with a text, immediately concerned. "Can I call you?"

"k," Kiyra typed back and Jenelle's phone responded with a *ding*.

"Did she forget everything about me?" Kiyra fumed as soon as she answered the phone call.

"What did she say to you?" Jenelle asked and her stomach involuntarily tightened, dreading to hear what her first *volunteer* had done.

"Is she clueless about what I've gone through? Or is she just stupid? Do you know what she asked me?" Kiyra snapped, not waiting for an answer from Jenelle to her previous questions.

"Tell me what happened," Jenelle requested and thought of a million things that could have gone wrong, but before she could get too far down the list, Kiyra continued her rampage.

"That dumb ass *casually* asked me why I was a prostitute? Why didn't I leave my pimp when I was dropped off to get my nails done?" Kiyra asked, firing off questions in rapid succession. "Does she actually think I was going to the salon? Like some suburban housewife?" Kiyra seethed.

"I'm shocked she said that to you," Jenelle offered with an apologetic voice, but she too was becoming angry with Dottie.

"That's when I let her have it," Kiyra huffed and continued, "I yelled at her in the restaurant. She was embarrassed, but I didn't care."

"You had a right to be upset," Jenelle agreed.

"Does she think I was making money? That I had freedom to come and go as I pleased? What did she think it was, *a job*? That I'd have my nails done and a makeover on my day off? Is she *out of her mind*?" Kiyra screamed into the phone.

"It was a mistake to have her talk to you."

"I didn't know what to expect, but it wasn't this."

"It's over now; you'll never have to talk to her again," Jenelle promised, trying to calm her down.

"You know what I've been through? You get me, right?" Kiyra pleaded, her anger dissipating and becoming despondent.

"Yes, I know you've been through a lot of horrible things, and I am going to help you through it," Jenelle assured her. She could hear Kiyra breathing hard on the other end of the phone.

"Doesn't she understand that I didn't have any money? I mean absolutely nothing in my pockets. Zero," Kiyra sobbed in a quieter voice and continued, "I didn't have a phone. I didn't have a purse to put anything in, let alone money that I didn't have."

"You had no control of your life," Jenelle reminded her and tried to hide her frustration with Dottie. She may have been well intended, but this meeting was a disaster.

"After they took me, I knew I was still in Greeley, but it was an area I'd never been to and had no clue where I was. It is not simple to walk away! They moved me from one cheap motel to another after a couple of days. And someone stood outside the motel room guarding the door. I never got to leave. I never saw the light of day. And she wonders why I didn't just walk away?"

Jenelle sensed that Kiyra needed to let out her emotions and get things off her chest, so she encouraged Kiyra to continue.

"I had nowhere to go. No one was looking for me because *no one cared about me*. Do you know what that feels like?" Kiyra asked, and Jenelle could hear her crying.

"It truly breaks my heart that you were treated like that and were so alone," Jenelle said, also becoming filled with emotion.

"Every day, they would pretty me up for some stranger. Guys would march into the motel room, one after the other. Oh, and did Dottie forget that I was thirteen and fourteen at the time?" Kiyra pointed out, her anger returning.

"What they did was cruel and evil," Jenelle said.

"When they were done with me, I'd finally get to eat. He decided what I ate, and when I ate it. I had to ask permission to go to the bathroom," Kiyra stated, her brokenness coming to the surface.

"Honestly, I don't know what's wrong with Dottie. Obviously, she's a dumbass. From now on it will be just you and me," she stated with an encouraging tone. "I'm on your side; you know that, right?" Jenelle asked.

"Yeah, I guess," Kiyra answered.

That's about as good of an answer that I could hope for at this time, Jenelle thought.

2 DAYS LATER, DECEMBER 20, 2017

"My volunteer is making me crazy. You're not going to believe what she posted on Facebook," Jenelle barked out and literally threw her purse onto the couch.

"What has Dottie done now?" Casey asked, knowing about Jenelle's recent phone call with Kiyra, and he understood that he was going to hear about it regardless of whether he wanted to or not.

"She wrote on Facebook before meeting up with Kiyra, and I quote: '*I am so excited that in two days I will meet with a sex trafficking victim. This is important work and this girl needs my help. It will be like having another granddaughter. I can't wait!*'"

"Was she expecting this girl to instantly trust her?" Casey wondered incredulously.

"It gets worse," Jenelle spoke in a frustrated and annoyed tone and continued, "You know that her meeting with Kiyra was a disaster, and then she writes today; listen to this: '*I had lunch with Kiyra Haas, but I can't figure out why she wasn't that receptive. I tried to convince her to do something better with her life other than prostitution. It is sad when people don't want to accept help.*'"

"She said her full name?" a flabbergasted Casey asked, "Do something better with her life? How stupid can she be?"

"Yes, can you believe this woman? Kiyra has been exploited for a year and a half and traumatized beyond belief, and Dottie is wondering why she seems distant and *isn't that receptive?*"

"She's out of her mind if she thinks a young girl chooses that life." Casey stated with building frustration.

"People think that Kiyra and girls like her are choosing to be in this lifestyle. It's unbelievable," Jenelle added.

"The whole women's sex work and empowerment movement helps hide the horrors and reality of sex trafficking," Casey observed.

"Exactly. Sure, there's plenty of strip clubs and some adult women providing peep shows on the internet, but that's different from *being forced into sex with strangers*," Jenelle stated.

"It doesn't help that the modern culture wants to legitimize prostitution and turn it into a career path," Casey replied.

"They conveniently forget the fact that many are underage, and by law, a minor is in no way capable of consenting."

"Yeah, movies like *Pretty Woman* are not real," Casey noted.

"No wonder Kiyra was ticked off at me. What's wrong with Dottie? I'm so pissed off at her," Jenelle fumed and let out a loud sigh. "Oh, and get this, she gave her a compass."

"A compass?"

"Yeah, like you would take for hiking. Kiyra had no idea what it was."

"Why did Dottie give her that?"

"So that if Kiyra ever needed direction in her life, *she'd be reminded to ask Dottie!*" Jenelle mocked with contempt.

"She's seen too many movies on the Hallmark Channel," Casey commented.

"Kiyra was right–this woman has lost her mind. She's so out of touch with reality. I really screwed this up," Jenelle replied.

"You can't control what other people say."

"But I talked to Dottie a long time about the issues of sex trafficking, how building trust is really hard and can take months, and sometimes never happens at all."

"She expected it to be like taking her granddaughter for lunch," Casey added.

"I think you're right. She's done talking with any of my clients," Jenelle replied and was still visibly frustrated and continued, "We talked about subjects to avoid. She showed no sensitivity or common sense."

"Kiyra probably thought she was condescending."

"Definitely. It's no wonder these girls don't trust anybody. Dottie was more interested in bragging to her friends about how she's *helping*," Jenelle stated, still wound up. "I finally got a hold of Dottie, and I just let her have it!"

"Good, she deserved it," Casey stated emphatically.

"I haven't cussed out someone like that in a while; honestly it felt good. And then she had the gall to say I wasn't a real Christian because I used profanity," Jenelle continued.

"She's making it about her. It's about the girl's trauma, not if some retiree gets her feelings hurt," Casey commented.

"She deserved everything I told her. This isn't some game."

"Exactly, she's treating it like a hobby," Casey replied.

"She isn't doing the hard work. You don't just have lunch with one of these girls and everything is solved," Jenelle noted.

"You'll have to be very picky about who you put in front of your clients in the future."

"That's for sure," Jenelle agreed. "It's hard work and it takes lots of time. I'd rather work twelve hours a day, seven days a week before I have someone like Dottie talk to one of my clients. I will spend more time screening my next volunteer."

"You need to clone yourself."

"Yeah. When they upset one of my girls it reflects badly on me.

They don't need any more trauma. Unless they trust me and my volunteers, the relationship goes nowhere."

"And ultimately that stops their growth as a survivor," Casey concluded.

2 DAYS LATER, DECEMBER 22, 2017

"How far can I get with this?" the young teen asked, flashing a twenty-dollar bill to the ticket agent. It'd taken her two hours to hitchhike to the Denver Greyhound bus terminal. She was *done*. Done with everyone and everything. Every bone in her body screamed with the full and complete knowledge *that it was time to go.*

"Is that one way or round trip?

"One way."

"Are you all right?" the ticket agent asked with some concern.

"How far can I get?" the girl asked again, ignoring the agent's question.

"Well, it's nineteen dollars to Greeley," the agent suggested and her slight concern easily morphed to indifference.

"Oh no, I'm not going to Greeley," she quickly answered. Greeley was due north of Denver, so she asked the agent for anything going south.

"There's a bus leaving for Pueblo in an hour. A one-way ticket costs seventeen dollars."

"Yeah, I'll take it," the teen answered without hesitation and moved her shoulder to more comfortably carry the small backpack which contained all her possessions. That left her with exactly thirty-six dollars in her pocket. She'd never been to Pueblo and didn't know anyone there. She didn't have a long-term plan and in fact, she didn't have a plan beyond the bus trip.

She pushed out the thoughts of the last time she was on the streets and had no realistic expectation that this was going to be a good choice. But for the moment, she had control of her life and could decide. Kiyra was solely focused on one thing and one thing only: *run.*

DECEMBER 24, 2017, 9:07 P.M.

The Highlands Ranch Town Center Shopping Mall, in a suburb of Denver, was abuzz with Christmas celebration and anticipation. Festive lights glowed and each store displayed its version of holiday cheer, all designed to draw in last-minute shoppers to find that perfect gift. Many stores extended their hours, and it was still somewhat busy at the late hour.

Bethany worked a twelve-hour shift at Starbucks and was glad to clean up the shop and soon head home. Long gone were the days when stores would close early on Christmas Eve. Corporate America wanted to squeeze every last dollar out of the season and keep people shopping until the last moment.

Her eyes were drawn to the Starbucks display, with its brightly colored coffee mugs in beautifully wrapped gift boxes. She never got tired of looking at the cheerful products. There were several plastic to-go containers to choose from that would be the final gift for her fifteen-year-old son. She smiled proudly to herself as he'd already started talking about going to college to become a registered nurse. Bethany had bigger dreams, where he'd put a *"Dr."* in front of his name.

But first things first, thought Bethany, as her son had not so subtly hinted about the twenty-four-ounce drink container with a built-in straw. It was perfect for containing his favorite Iced Frappuccino.

This was going to be a magical Christmas, she thought to herself. The whole family would be getting together. The house would smell of food cooking, and holiday treats coming out of the oven.

This was her favorite time of the year. Customers were a little more friendly and all the bright lights and shiny ornaments made these past two weeks special.

She truly felt warmth in her heart, for herself and her cherished family. She looked forward to tomorrow, spending the entire day with her relatives, first going to church and then enjoying a lavish meal–and sharing good cheer. She was living the dream of the perfect suburban American family. She even had the good fortune to enjoy carolers at the store earlier who sang her favorite song, "Silent Night." She felt good because life in fact *was good*. She felt content and had no reason to sense anything different.

As she started sweeping up the floor, she noticed a woman getting out of a car. This caught her eye because she was dressed provocatively without a coat, and that was especially unusual at this time of night when the temperatures dropped.

The woman walked by the storefront window, headed towards a different section of the parking lot, and her face was expressionless, as if in a daze and was going through the motions. Her face communicated a sense of dread, the polar opposite of what Bethany was feeling inside.

For a moment, a thought came into her mind. *Something's not right. Is this woman in trouble?* But she wasn't a woman, realizing this was clearly a teen who was wearing too much makeup. *Why is she dressed up like that and all alone in an empty parking lot?*

Bethany watched the girl step into the back of an older Lexus packed with several men. The door closed, and the car immediately pulled away. Bethany scoffed at her outfit and was glad she didn't have a daughter, and then refocused on her cleaning tasks as she had to get home to people who loved her.

1 MINUTE EARLIER

"We're going to drop you off here. You see that Lexus over there?"

"The silver car?"

"No stupid, the Lexus," he shouted and smacked the back of her head. "It's the dark-colored, four-door right in front of Starbucks."

"Yeah, I see it," the girl answered.

"They're going to pick you up. They're going to have you for twelve hours, and you're gonna do whatever you need to do to make them happy, you hear?" Marcus growled with contempt.

"Twelve hours?"

"Yeah. Timo and his boys want you for an entire evening. I was nice enough to give them the group rate. It's Christmas after all," he sneered with scorn.

Anything could happen in twelve hours! ANYTHING at all, she screamed to herself, but only muttered, "Okay."

"Okay? Girl, you're lucky I got you this all-night gig! Business slows down around Christmas, so you should be thanking me for setting this up for you. You ain't no good to me if you're sitting around on Christmas, not earning your keep," he reminded her. As he was talking, his face shifted into the shadows, projecting an intimidating evil glow on his face.

"Yeah," she answered in defeat. What choice did she have?

"You do what you're told. I take care of you and this is how you take care of me. You don't want me angry at you, do you?"

"No," she answered. That was the last thing she wanted.

"You make sure that you're so good that they'll want you again for New Year's Eve. I'll charge full price for that. If you don't make that happen, there'll be hell to pay," he threatened and his voice started to rise in volume as his words bounced off the car's window.

"Yeah, I got it," she answered and stepped out of the car and slowly started the long and lonely walk towards the Lexus.

He lowered the car window and told her with disgust and sarcasm, "Hey Shanice, you have a *real good* time!"

* * *

The problem's plain to see, too much technology
Machines to save our lives, machines dehumanize
Secret, secret, I got a secret

"Mr. Roboto" - Styx

PART 3, TESSA

Kelly was pregnant at nineteen when they decided to get married. Tim wasn't enthusiastic about the baby, the marriage, or anything else. Kelly hoped that his heart would melt once he saw his daughter's innocent and beautiful face. Tessa was perfect. Kelly longingly wished for Tim's hardened heart to soften up.

But if anything, the opposite occurred. Once Tessa was born, Tim only saw his daughter as another mouth to feed and another body to clothe. Tessa was a noisy distraction, taking time away from his true passion, which was finding the bottom of a liquor bottle. Although he was not abusive towards his small family, he easily found reasons to be absent, frequently drinking with his friends and complaining about his lack of job opportunities.

On the opposite end of the spectrum, Kelly was constantly hovering over the girl, feeling like a single parent. She imposed her complete control over Tessa's life. While that may have been fine when she was a toddler, her overbearing nature didn't change as Tessa grew into a teenager.

Kelly worked the checkout register at the local Walmart, with most of her paycheck going towards the household expenses because Tim's employment and financial contribution were inconsistent. Kelly felt trapped and frustrated. Her only bright spot was her daughter. She literally and figuratively clung to her and rarely let go.

Tim and Kelly begrudgingly stayed in a loveless marriage that resembled two roommates who had a child together. Although the family dynamics weren't ideal, Tessa was cared for and received the basic necessities, albeit provided by an overbearing mother and a distant father. That situation left a small crack in the family's thin armor protecting their precious girl.

SEPTEMBER 2019

Raising a teenage girl is never easy, and the reaction to a mom's control is sometimes met with rebellion. Or the teen's desire to escape. In Tessa's case, she chose to escape through video games.

Not only could she enter an exciting world created by software programmers, but there were so many new and interesting people to meet online. And there was the added perk that she could create an online persona and become anyone she wanted to be. It never occurred to Tessa that the other gamers may not be truthful in their online profile.

During the summer after Tessa turned fifteen, she became enthralled with playing *Minecraft* on her Xbox console. She joined some groups, and one day received an instant message from another gamer. It all started out innocent enough.

Tessa was bragging about her gaming skills in a chat room, which opened the door for another player to ask for Tessa's expert advice. No one ever asked Tessa for advice on anything, so this attention fed her fragile young ego. The gamer suggested they enter a private chat room and she was excited to receive attention from an older boy.

Soon, conversations went beyond playing the game, and started to get personal. Her new online *friend* was asking easy and simple questions, such as what foods she liked, types of clothes she wore, and her favorite music. Tessa was amazed that her new "boy" friend had similar likes and dislikes. She was genuinely happy that they were so compatible, and she looked forward to chatting daily with her new friend Jimmy.

A few weeks and a thousand chat messages later, Jimmy professed that he was falling for Tessa. She responded that she too was developing real feelings. He asked her for a favor. He wanted to know if he could call Tessa his *girlfriend*. She squealed in delight and quickly agreed. Over the next few weeks, game playing became secondary because the two were constantly messaging each other, feeding their budding romance.

Jimmy eventually asked Tessa what town she lived in and she answered that it was Littleton, CO. She couldn't believe her luck that Jimmy also lived in Colorado, in nearby Aurora. Then one day, Jimmy asked to meet with her in person. He suggested getting together at the Cherry Creek Mall. Tessa figured that was a safe place and didn't have any reason to be suspicious since he didn't ask for her home address. She responded that she also wanted to meet.

The new school year had already started, so they agreed to meet over the upcoming weekend. Tessa felt incredibly fortunate that of all the places Jimmy could live, he was in a nearby city. Even more exhilarating, Jimmy had a gift card to Hollister that was about to expire, and he wanted to spend it on his new *girlfriend*. Life was good!

Tessa couldn't wait for Saturday afternoon to arrive. During this time, she didn't mention anything about Jimmy to her parents. But then why would she? Her father couldn't care less about what was happening in her life. Would she talk to her mother?

Forget it! Tessa knew she'd insist on meeting Jimmy, and *the last thing* she wanted was for her mother to scare Jimmy out of her life.

Tessa lied to her mother and said she was meeting friends from school at the mall, so the request seemed normal except that this particular mall was more upscale than the family budget normally allowed. Tessa didn't ask for money, so her mom assumed that the outing would only be window shopping.

"Are you looking for a new pair of jeans?" Kelly asked, knowing that her daughter had been complaining about her lack of designer clothing.

"I don't know, maybe," Tessa answered in a dismissive tone. She didn't want to have a conversation with her mother. She just needed a ride.

"I could come in with you, and we can do some shopping before you meet up with your friends," she suggested.

"No, mom, forget it," Tessa answered, annoyed that her mother would suggest such an embarrassing situation. Shopping with mom? No way.

"We never go shopping together anymore," Kelly replied.

"I'm fifteen. I think I can shop for myself. I'm only going so I can hang out with my friends," Tessa answered emphatically, shutting down any chance of her mother tagging along. They approached the mall and Tessa jumped out of the car and quickly closed the door behind her, without saying goodbye.

* * *

They were to meet at the food court and Tessa told Jimmy exactly what she'd be wearing, so he instantly recognized her and said, "You must be Tessa."

"Yes?" she answered with an elongated tone that communicated her confusion.

"When you said you were fifteen, I thought you were joking. You sounded so mature," Jimmy said with a warm and easy smile. "I thought for sure you were seventeen or eighteen."

"Well, you're more than two years older than me," she noted, still confused why her boyfriend Jimmy had a scruffy beard, dressed in baggy pants with a plain t-shirt, and looked about twenty pounds overweight.

"You're right, I just turned thirty," he lied. "I received a $100 gift card for my birthday. Do you want to go shopping?" Jimmy asked, ignoring the deception about his age.

"I guess," Tessa replied, thinking that this guy should buy her a new pair of jeans for lying to her.

"We can't be boyfriend and girlfriend," he told her with conviction, putting Tessa's mind at ease. "You're too young for me. And *too pretty*," he said smiling, giving her a wink.

"Okay," she replied, unable to think of anything else to say.

"Hollister is down this way." He gestured to his left, and they started walking. "Why don't you call me Uncle Jimmy," he suggested.

"Sure, whatever," she said and rolled her eyes.

Uncle Jimmy was in fact forty-three years old. As they were shopping, he suggested that she think of him as her *favorite uncle*. Since her parents never bought her name-brand clothing, it wasn't that much of a stretch for Tessa to immediately latch on to her rich new uncle. After shopping for an hour, she was thrilled to have new clothes. He led them to a bench outside the store and he offered her gummy bears.

"These are pretty good," she said approvingly.

"Yes, they are," he heartily agreed and ate one of the gummies he purchased from the local marijuana dispensary.

"You know, you're a great gamer, but you could be even better if you were more relaxed," he told her.

"How do I do that?" she asked.

"All the top gamers, they take this vitamin," he told her and showed her a small pill.

"Just a vitamin?"

"Of course, all the best players do. It's totally safe," he said and placed the pill in his mouth and took a drink of water. "Try it. I guarantee you'll play better and all your troubles will melt away."

"I don't know," she answered with some hesitation.

He handed her a pill and gestured for her to consume the Oxycontin. Once she did, they walked the mall for a little bit longer until he told her it was time for him to go. She was a little disappointed that the afternoon ended so quickly. Tessa planned to tell her mom that the clothes were bought on sale. Maybe Tessa would be lucky and her mom wouldn't have any questions.

The next day, Uncle Jimmy messaged her to see if she liked the *vitamin*. He offered to meet her after school and get her some more. She thought nothing of it and agreed. It soon became a routine three times a week and Tessa looked forward to getting more pills from her favorite uncle. She enjoyed the attention from him and everything was great, *until the day it wasn't.*

One afternoon, Uncle Jimmy told Tessa that he was out of vitamins. Tessa was disappointed, but he then reassured her that her favorite uncle would take care of her. *He had something better.* He convinced her to get in his car and promised to later take her home. He'd been the perfect uncle, and built a level of trust with Tessa, so it didn't take much persuading. He went to an empty parking lot a mile away.

Uncle Jimmy had been waiting for this moment from the first time he messaged her. He was so excited with anticipation that his hands were somewhat shaky and his voice cracked as he lit up a glass shard in his meth pipe and instructed her to try it. She hesitated and shook her head.

"I have asthma," she stated and showed him an inhaler she always kept in her pocket.

"Don't worry, this won't make it worse," Uncle Jimmy told her with an air of authority. "In fact, you'll feel better."

"Are you sure?" she asked, still unsure of what he had in his pipe.

"Just try it," he coaxed in a stern voice. Here was the test. Would she run away? Or did he groom her well enough that she desired his approval?

She didn't move for a few seconds and then spoke. "How do I do this?"

Uncle Jimmy smiled, lifted the pipe slowly towards his mouth, and calmly answered, "Like this."

Within half an hour, Tessa was asking for another hit. Within a week, she was hooked on meth. Within another week, she figured out which kids in school were taking drugs. She became instantly popular with those kids because Uncle Jimmy was supplying her with a variety of edible marijuana products, alcohol, Oxycontin, and methamphetamine that she'd sometimes share with her friends.

Her new party friends were delighted and they quickly accepted her into the group. Within a month she was getting high almost daily and couldn't stop. A few weeks later, Tessa never could remember how she lost her virginity on her sixteenth birthday to one of her fellow high school tweakers.

Her parents noticed that her behavior changed and her grades plummeted. She became short-tempered, argumentative, and just plain nasty. This drove her father to be even more distant, not wanting to deal with any teenage girl drama, so she instead argued with her mother. Constantly. Kelly chalked it up to normal teenage rebellion, and the more controlling she tried to be, the more Tessa rebelled. Strong rules and discipline were not working.

Her favorite uncle set these actions in motion. He relished hearing stories from Tessa that her mom was always on her case and how she hated her parents. He would be the anti-parent. He constantly told her how he was the only one who understood and supported her.

Tessa kept running back to her Uncle Jimmy who understood her and made her feel special when they hung out in his apartment. She loved the way he was always looking out for her, taking care of her, and most importantly, how he fed her addiction out of the goodness of his heart. The drugs were always available for free, *until the day they weren't.*

2 MONTHS LATER, NOVEMBER 2019

Tessa was desperate for her drugs and was surprised and perturbed that her favorite uncle taunted her. He waved the meth pipe in front of her face and laughed at her.

"You know you want it," he goaded.

"Yeah, so just give it to me," she pleaded.

"What will you do for me if I give it to you? *I have needs too, you know.*"

"You want me to pay you? You've never asked for money before," Tessa exclaimed with confusion.

"I don't want money; I want something *else*," Uncle Jimmy hissed, and the normally jovial look on his face disappeared. His eyes appeared black and formidable and his jaw clenched with the resolve of someone who was tired of playing the nice uncle charade. It was time to get down to business.

Tessa became nervous because she hadn't seen this side of her favorite uncle. He was not joking around, and she feared there was no going back to the nice old Uncle Jimmy.

"What do you want?" she asked innocently but wouldn't admit

why she got a sick feeling in the pit of her stomach and the hair on the back of her neck stood up. The resigned look on her face projected what Uncle Jimmy already knew: sixteen-year-old Tessa was going to do whatever it took to get the meth pipe.

"How bad do you want this?" he mocked her. "Real bad?"

"You know I want it. Come on, hand it over," she asserted with her body craving the ever-elusive high of methamphetamines.

"You can start by taking your shirt off," he instructed in a serious tone, his eyes fixated on her upper body. Since she'd known him, he never laid a hand on her. But she noticed that recently, he was getting more sexually suggestive. Tessa was surprised he was so direct.

But at this point, she didn't care. The pull of the drugs was too strong. And she was going to smoke that pipe one way or another. She recalled the sultry appearance of models from *Cosmopolitan* magazine and did her best to mimic their look.

Uncle Jimmy smiled and nodded with approval, so she continued. She knew instinctively that she'd have to give him what he needed, which was more than a peek at her breasts. Then she would get what she needed.

She slowly lifted her shirt over her head. Jimmy's grooming plan worked to perfection. After her favorite uncle was done with her, he gave her more meth and started making phone calls.

It registered in her mind that she'd traded sex for drugs, which seemed wrong, but she decided that if she was going to give a man what he wanted, she might as well get something out of it. Her mind and body were solely focused on getting high, so any rationale would be acceptable.

Tessa entered the world of forced prostitution two hours later. Her favorite uncle continually gave her drugs that evening, and she was too deliriously high to notice that he was collecting money from strangers to have sex with her.

There wasn't much discussion, but Tessa understood that she now worked for Uncle Jimmy, and he would continue her supply of drugs. Tessa was sixteen, blossoming with the curves of womanhood, and had a natural beauty that made her a very desirable target. Her cute round face framed by her jet-black hair was simultaneously sultry and innocent so it wasn't hard for Uncle Jimmy to keep her busy after school and on weekends.

Tessa's parents were used to her not being home much and she had free reign to come and go as she pleased. They continued to be in denial even after she'd been suspended from school because of drug use. They knew she partied too much on the weekends and convinced themselves she was just a rebellious teenager and would eventually grow out of it.

Tessa's parents wouldn't look any deeper to see that she was completely out of control, and her parents were even becoming afraid of Tessa's constant outbursts and verbal abuse. They were relieved when Tessa was not at home.

When Tessa took drugs or drank alcohol, she became angry and took a sadistic pleasure in being cruel and hurtful. The drugs and constant sexual abuse altered her personality, but her parents couldn't see that this provided cover for her real pain. Tessa's mood swings made it easy to hide her life of being sex trafficked.

On a cold January night in 2020, Tessa and one of her friends went to a party, and around 2:00 a.m., her friend passed out. That left Tessa, by default, to use the friend's car to drive them home. Tessa was barely able to function and didn't know how to drive a car, and less than a mile from the party, she took a corner too wide, jumped the curb, and hit a traffic light pole, landing her thirty days in a juvenile detention center.

The warning signs fell through the cracks of government bureaucracy, so her life as a sex slave did not surface to the authorities. She agreed to attend drug rehab and counseling in order to receive a lighter sentence, and she was back home in a week.

Tessa's parents were exhausted from constantly fighting with their daughter and were simply counting the days until she became eighteen and could be out on her own, and out of their house. Tessa had a hard time remembering her life before her drug addiction and sex trafficking.

But no matter how much trouble Tessa got in, it wasn't enough motivation to kick her drug addiction. And since she didn't have any money or a job, there was only one way she could get her drugs. And that was from her *favorite uncle*.

But Tessa wasn't the first girl that Uncle Jimmy had control over. Uncle Jimmy found three runaways who were under his control and living with him in his small apartment. Tessa was the only one still residing at home and going to school, but that didn't provide her any more freedom or comfort. She still had to bring in her quota for her favorite uncle or she wouldn't get any drugs.

In February of 2020, Uncle Jimmy was in the hallway outside his apartment, arguing loudly with one of the men who just finished paying to have sex with Tessa. A pair of police officers were questioning a neighbor about an unrelated domestic violence case when they saw the altercation with Uncle Jimmy.

The door to the apartment was open, and the officers saw a young-looking girl engaged in sex on the couch with a middle-aged man. That was all the probable cause they needed to enter the apartment. Later that evening, Uncle Jimmy was arrested and his operation was shut down. Over the last four months of being under his control, Tessa was forced into prostitution by Uncle Jimmy *a total of 412 times*.

James Arianas Dollymomus, known on the street as *Uncle Jimmy*, was charged with multiple counts of *human trafficking of a minor for sexual servitude.* Besides Tessa, two other underage girls and one boy were discovered by the police in Uncle Jimmy's apartment. All three were runaways, but only the two girls were reported as missing. The boy was living in a foster home, but he was never reported missing after he ran away.

For the moment, Tessa was no longer being trafficked, but more pressing for Tessa was that her source for drugs had dried up. She immediately turned to shoplifting to feed her habit. One night, she stole her parent's car to drive to her new drug dealer for heroin, meth, and beer, but on her way back home she crashed into a parked car and was again arrested.

As part of her sentence, the judge ordered that she wear an ankle bracelet. The SCRAM (secure continuous remote alcohol monitor) bracelet had GPS monitoring and measured alcohol intake by testing the wearer's sweat. SCRAM devices measure and upload data to a monitoring agency or company. Although it couldn't test for drugs, authorities would know if she'd consumed any alcohol, and the GPS would constantly indicate her whereabouts. Tessa managed to avoid alcohol to obtain clean readings, but the device wouldn't detect heroin or meth, her drug of choice.

1 MONTH LATER, MARCH 2020

Tessa was late for her court-required appointment, and Jenelle peered towards the front door of the building to see if she was approaching. Jenelle didn't have formal office space, so one of the larger local nonprofits allowed her to meet Tessa in their office. The conference rooms were occupied, but there was an empty cubicle that would allow for some privacy.

Tessa was going to be a hard nut to crack, not that Jenelle had any uncomplicated or effortless clients. There was no such thing as an *easy case.* Plenty of clients were non-communicative and showed up for the sole purpose of logging time to fulfill a court requirement.

But Tessa was worse than that because most of the time she was high on something. Jenelle saw track marks on her arms from heroin use. For most of their prior four meetings, Tessa sat in her chair like a zombie, barely saying a word. If she did say anything, her remarks would be laced with biting sarcasm.

Tessa finally arrived and for once looked sober. *Maybe we can have a real conversation,* Jenelle thought to herself.

"Hello," Jenelle said in a somewhat upbeat tone. Tessa looked down and didn't respond. After a full minute of silence, Jenelle added, "Okay, if that's how it is going to be, I am going to get some paperwork done." And that's exactly what Jenelle proceeded to do.

Neither one said anything further over the next twenty-two minutes. Jenelle eventually looked up casually and saw Tessa agitated, gritting her teeth and clenching her fists. This type of client behavior was common and before she could make a comment, Tessa started talking.

"You think you're so perfect," Tessa blurted out with sarcasm.

"Me? What are you talking about?"

"You, with your perfect blonde hair, skinny jeans, manicured nails, and the fancy diamond ring. You probably have the perfect husband too!"

She ignored the comments and said in a gentle manner, "Sweetie, we all have flaws; we all have problems we're dealing with."

"You have no idea," Tessa answered, still agitated, and shook her head to get her hair out of her eyes, momentarily revealing the entire neck tattoo that Uncle Jimmy had branded her with.

"I work with a lot of girls that've been in your situation, and all of them had challenges moving forward," Jenelle reassured her.

"You don't know anything about me and have no idea what it's like to be a teenager today. What are you, like fifty years old?" she screeched.

"Tessa, we're here to talk about you, not me," she redirected, ignoring the insults.

"You want to talk about me? You think you can help me?" she seethed incredulously. "You are only here because you have to."

Because I have to? You think I'm getting paid for this? I run a nonprofit, with emphasis on the no-profit, Jenelle thought to herself, outwardly calm and inwardly keeping her frustration in check. She paused to determine how to respond, but Tessa kept talking.

"You're only here because it's court-ordered. You probably live in a big fancy house, so who are you fooling?" Tessa attacked.

"I don't get a dime for doing this. You're trying to deflect the issues."

"Well, aren't you just the special woman, helping all the poor dumb whores like me," Tessa sneered, oozing with sarcasm while condemning herself.

"What happened to you was not your fault. You're a victim of human trafficking, but it doesn't mean you get to treat me like shit," Jenelle countered, allowing herself to display her annoyance.

"Hmph," Tessa responded and folded her arms in infuriated disbelief.

"You can be mean to me all you want, but as I told you before, that's what I do. I help kids like you get set up with the right resources to straighten out their life."

"You think I need help? You think my life is screwed up? I'm doing just fine. I don't need you or your *help*. I only need everyone to get off my back," Tessa complained and continued, "I certainly don't need *Miss Perfect* telling me what to do."

"I think it's pretty obvious that you can't manage your life, otherwise you wouldn't be here. Come on, Tessa, stop trying to argue with me, and let's come up with a plan," urged Jenelle. "The first thing you need to do is get sober," she advised and reached out her hand to comfort the teen, but Tessa backed away.

"That's the only way I can get through the day, don't you get it?" Tessa seethed.

Jenelle felt Tessa's genuine fear about not finding her next high, her escape. Such fear dominated Tessa's focus and attention. The last thing Tessa wanted was someone blocking her escape route. The building anger was reaching the boiling point and was about to be directed at the one person that could stand in her way. Tessa reacted in the only way that she knew how: *energized anger.*

Jenelle recognized the look on her face, which was a combination of fear and frustration wrapped around white-hot hatred. Tessa was hurt deeply and the pain manifested itself in the only way that Tessa knew how to process it. She had to hurt someone else.

Tessa thought to herself, *I'm going to literally scratch her eyes out, and I'm going to enjoy it.* She quickly stood up and lunged toward Jenelle. Jenelle anticipated her actions but wasn't fast enough to get out of her chair. Tessa immediately tackled Jenelle, still sitting in her chair. They both fell backwards and crashed into the flimsy cubicle wall, knocking it down and they both landed with a thud.

Tessa immediately grabbed Jenelle's hair to wreak havoc and pull her closer so she could stick her long fingernails into Jenelle's eyeballs. She was on a mission, and she had only one thing on her mind and that was to *inflict pain.*

Tessa's lip curled upwards and she wailed at Jenelle like an animal in the jungle. Tessa simply wanted to cause destruction. It was a release of raw energy. "I'm going to kill you!" Tessa yelled and had visions of getting on top of Jenelle, digging her fingers into her, and popping out her eyeballs. She needed to see blood.

Tessa wanted Jenelle to suffer like she'd never suffered before. She sought to destroy and obliterate her perfect life. *Let's see you try to be miss helpful when you're blind and your face is crushed in,* thought Tessa.

But before Tessa's fantasy of sinister rage could come true, an office staff member came over and pulled Tessa off Jenelle. She was still on the floor, crouching on all fours and curling her fingernails at them, gesturing her desire to rip flesh down to the bone.

Within another few seconds, several other people showed up, which aggravated Tessa even more and enraged her to the point that her brain could not process what was going on. She wanted to lash out and was frustrated with her missed opportunity.

Both Tessa and Jenelle were still on the floor and breathing hard. Jenelle put her hands up in a defensive position in case Tessa attacked again, but Tessa's adrenaline was dissipating.

"It's okay–give us some space," she instructed the staff and turned to look at Tessa. Jenelle could tell that Tessa was starting to run out of energy, and then added, "Take a few steps back." They cautiously retreated.

Tessa curled up in the fetal position on the floor and tried to control her breathing. She took out her asthma inhaler but fumbled with it and it dropped to the floor.

"Calm down, it's okay," Jenelle told her and she grabbed the inhaler and fed it to Tessa who rested her head in Jenelle's lap. Tessa breathed deeply, and it helped her cool down.

Jenelle gently stroked her hair and could tell Tessa was getting close to a normal breathing pace. But the agitation on Tessa's face turned to sadness. Jenelle continued to compose herself, still shocked by how quickly Tessa became enraged and how fast she'd tackled her. Jenelle wouldn't notice her shoulder pain until a few hours later.

Tessa realized that it was over, and all her actions had resulted in nothing more than a release of energy. Yet she didn't feel better about anything. *She'd accomplished nothing.*

Tessa soon fully transitioned from attack mode into protection mode. The last thing she wanted to do was to go back to juvenile hall. She didn't want to be locked up, and although it was possible to obtain drugs there, it would be more expensive and cash was something she didn't have, and she loathed the thought of again trading her body for drugs.

"I'm sorry, okay?" Tessa implored and started crying from her release of emotion and her desire to invoke sympathy. She looked up and begged, "Please don't tell my probation officer." Jenelle continued stroking her hair.

4 DAYS LATER

If Jenelle was expecting any regret or contriteness from Tessa, it was quickly dispelled when Tessa refused to speak at their next session.

"I should have told your probation officer, but I didn't," Jenelle offered and received an blank stare in response. Tessa's expression clearly communicated that she wanted to be somewhere else.

Jenelle tried to engage her in conversation and was again met with a blank stare. And Jenelle thought, *If you want to be quiet, fine, I'll be quieter.* Tessa shifted in her chair and looked down.

Jenelle had nothing left to do but catch up on paperwork, which kept her busy for the next two sessions, because Tessa did not utter a word.

9 DAYS LATER

"What's this?" Tessa asked as Jenelle handed her a pumpkin spice latte.

Jenelle raised her eyebrows in slight surprise that Tessa had spoken. Encouraged by that, she said, "It's for you; I thought you would enjoy it."

Out of habit, Tessa looked at the beverage with suspicion. She put the coffee up to her nose and let the aroma waft towards her. It was indeed a pumpkin spice latte. She took a small sip. And then another and licked her lips and purred, "Thanks."

"You're welcome," Jenelle responded and continued, "You have a beautiful smile. You really do." Tessa grinned but then looked away.

Jenelle sensed the wall was melting just a little and wanted to go further. "Tessa, we've had our ups and downs; okay, maybe just the downs," she jested.

"Yeah," Tessa playfully admitted and took another sip of the sweet beverage.

"I know you're hurting, and I'm here for you. You can make it to the other side," Jenelle stated and then asked gently, "Can I tell you a story about a girl I worked with?"

"I guess," Tessa answered. Jenelle proceeded for the next twenty minutes to explain everything Sierra had gone through and most importantly how Sierra became a survivor.

"Your journey will be different, but you can get there," Jenelle told the teen.

"Maybe," Tessa answered reluctantly, searching for hope.

"I wish you'd show me the person you're trying so hard to hide. I know you want to protect her, but if you let me in, maybe you will be able to trust again."

"It's too hard most of the time. I'm only sixteen, but I feel like I've lived twice that long."

"Trust is a slow thing to earn, but we'll work together as a team," Jenelle reiterated and thought to herself that she'd finally made some progress.

264 DAYS LATER, DECEMBER 2020

The tough journey for Tessa continued. She was placed in an alternate high school, which was a fancy name for kids who had behavior problems or a criminal record. In the old days, it would be called a reform school. All the kids in her new school had a troubled past, and Tessa didn't feel unique or singled out in that respect.

Some of the teens were still making bad decisions and there were always several kids who one day showed up and others who one day simply disappeared. The revolving door was the norm.

Tessa's relationship was tenuous with her parents, and the only success that anyone could claim is that she didn't run away and was no longer involved in forced prostitution. Her parents had no idea how to deal with Tessa, and the problems of the past year had worn them out, and they had given up on their only child.

Through a combination of quality and quantity of time, Jenelle gained Tessa's trust, which allowed Tessa to talk through her issues and see a plan for her future. Jenelle became her personal cheerleader and encouraged all the small positive steps. She was also there to cry with Tessa after her inevitable setbacks. Tessa had a lot of energy and fire, but she needed help channeling it in a positive way.

With Tessa's drug addiction, Jenelle was concerned that she'd be influenced by the wrong crowd or fall into depression and attempt to self-medicate, which would crush her fragile sobriety. There was the real possibility that Tessa could return to heroin and methamphetamine and use her body to feed her drug habit. It was like walking on the edge of a cliff, and it wouldn't take much to go over. So far, her stumbles were minor and her days of being a survivor were growing.

Tessa was in constant communication with Jenelle who helped navigate government agencies and other nonprofits that helped Tessa, including her drug rehabilitation program. The trial date for Uncle Jimmy was delayed several times due to the coronavirus, but as it came closer, it was starting to weigh on Tessa.

"I'm going to testify," Tessa explained in a nervous tone while she and Jenelle were sitting at a coffee shop.

"That's not going to be easy, but I will be there in the courtroom for moral support."

"Sure, that'd be okay with me," Tessa replied, but clearly would appreciate a friendly face in the audience.

"I'll be there. You've been through so much. You're one of the toughest people I know. This is your chance to help put this guy away."

"Yeah, I know," Tessa acknowledged without much faith, "but what if he's let go?"

"I won't lie to you, sweetie, that's always a possibility, but Officer Barnes told me they have a strong case."

"I don't think I can handle it if he's let free," Tessa fretted and let out a loud sigh. "I will freak out if I see him on the streets somewhere and get put back in the life."

"Relax. Breathe," Jenelle instructed as she saw Tessa on the verge of triggering an asthma attack. "It's going to be all right."

"I don't know, is it?" she squeaked and wiped her eyes that were tearing.

"Yes, I will be with you every step of the way, from working with the prosecutor, the police, and your testimony at trial."

"Okay," Tessa answered and seemed to shrink in her chair.

"You're a strong girl. We both know that," Jenelle pressed, sensing that Tessa needed to be propped up. "If you are uncomfortable in the courtroom, you find me. You stare at the look on my face. My expression will encourage you to be fearless. *I have faith in you.*"

Tessa looked at Jenelle and knew she had someone with unwavering support in her corner and said with a deep sense of combined sadness and happiness, "You're the only person I can count on."

"It's you and me against the world. I'm not going anywhere," Jenelle stressed.

Jenelle realized Tessa's story was far from over and there would be days that Tessa would move backwards, but she was worth it. Jenelle also knew that Tessa needed someone to keep her feet moving in the right direction, and unfortunately, Tessa was right, she didn't have anyone else that was committed to helping her.

55 DAYS LATER, FEBRUARY 2021

"They are coming back into the courtroom," Jenelle texted. Tessa was too stressed to be there when the jury rendered the verdict, so she opted to have Jenelle relay the results. Both were on pins and needles waiting for the answer. Testifying in court was painful and difficult, but Tessa understood that it was a necessary step for her to move on.

Both Tessa and Jenelle realized that the verdict was going to change Tessa's life. Like a rudder on a sailboat, whichever way the verdict went, it was going to veer Tessa's future in a particular direction.

She continued to struggle with depression-induced relapses back into drugs and alcohol. It was a daily challenge, and Tessa wasn't fully comfortable with the structured routine of her alternative high school, and not surprisingly, she habitually rebelled against discipline and authority. However, even with the setbacks, her life was slowly resembling normalcy.

"They are reading it now," Jenelle quickly typed and soon excitedly texted, "Guilty on all counts!"

"Are you fucking kidding me???" Tessa responded.

"No, I am not! They are taking him away right now."

"OMG!!!" she replied in her text and let out a verbal squeal of delight that turned some heads in her study hall. "Can you come over after school?"

"I'll pick you up," Jenelle responded.

* * *

Jenelle saw Tessa sitting on a bench and pulled her car into a parking space near the front of the school. As she approached, she instantly noticed Tessa was crying. Jenelle sat down and immediately gestured, "Come here," and Tessa leaned over and hugged her.

"Tell me what's going through your head," she prompted.

"I don't know, a little bit of everything. I'm glad that he was convicted, but I still don't feel like it's over," Tessa exclaimed.

"Well, it isn't over for you," Jenelle remarked.

"No, but for the first time, I don't want to blame myself."

"You're not responsible for his actions. He planned to manipulate you before you two ever met," she reassured Tessa.

"I know, but I need to keep hearing it."

"I understand, and if it helps, I'll remind you every day," Jenelle stated and smiled.

"Okay," Tessa answered and returned the smile. "I know I can count on you."

"Now that he's convicted, you'll never have to see him again."

"Yes, he's the one going to prison; he's the bad one, not me," Tessa stated calmly with the slightest hint of confidence and peace.

"The prosecutor expects him to get over sixty years of prison time. He's likely to die in there," Jenelle replied.

"Good," Tessa whispered.

Throughout their relationship, Jenelle saw Tessa's shame and regret, and they'd worked through those issues. And now finally, Jenelle saw harmony and thankfulness. It was in her eyes, and Jenelle's gut told her that Tessa turned a corner. The conviction of her captor was the vindication and conclusion that Tessa needed to let go of the pain. She could envision Tessa graduating high school and becoming a well-put-together young adult.

Today was a good day, thought Jenelle.

432 DAYS LATER, APRIL 23, 2022

"'Tis the season for pumpkin spiced latte's, don't you think?" Jenelle mused as she handed Tessa her coffee.

"It's always the season. You know me so well," Tessa acknowledged with a smile. "Before you ask, I am going to tell you that things are going well."

"That's awesome!" Jenelle beamed and nodded her head, amazed at the progress this young woman had made.

"That was so cool of you to get me one of these drinks that first time," Tessa said.

"You were pretty difficult for a while," Jenelle teased as two old friends would banter, comfortable in their friendship.

"I was pretty crabby back then."

"Especially when you had to wear the ankle bracelet."

"I didn't make the best decisions when I was high. Duh!" Tessa exclaimed and rolled her eyes to poke fun at herself.

"Like I've always told you, if you play stupid games, you win stupid prizes."

"Yeah, and I had to wear that prize for six months! You put up with me even when I tackled you," she stated and laughed.

"You are supposed to tackle your problems, not me!" Jenelle joked back.

"I know, right? I thought I was trying out for the Broncos!" Tessa giggled with a big smile.

"It's so good to see you like this."

"Honestly, I don't know why you kept helping me when I was pushing you away," Tessa inquired in a more serious tone.

"I was hoping we'd get to this point, although there were times when it didn't seem like it was ever going to happen."

"I didn't think it would either. I'm amazed at how much my life has changed since *he* was put away," Tessa admitted.

"The important thing is that you allowed me to help you, but *you* did the work."

"Yeah, and after he was convicted, I knew that if I didn't turn it around right then and there, I would lose what was left of me, and lose it forever."

"You did the hard work and look at you now, graduating from high school next month. I am so proud of you," Jenelle told her.

"Thanks. It is good to be back at my old high school instead of that alternative one."

"Did you enroll for the summer semester at community college?" Jenelle asked.

"I sure did."

"Good for you. Have you decided what you're going to study?" Jenelle inquired.

"I'm going to work towards a degree in criminal justice. I talked to Officer Barnes and told him that I hoped one day to work with him."

"Wow, that's impressive," Jenelle exclaimed.

"I want to thank you for not giving up on me."

"The thing you always have to remember is that you were worth the effort."

"Well, thanks anyway," Tessa replied.

"Wait, isn't the prom tonight?" Jenelle asked.

"Yes!" Tessa exclaimed in delight. "I bought this super cute light blue dress. Oh, and the shoes, I have to tell you about the shoes!" she said with glee and her eyes sparkled with the excited anticipation of a typical teenager.

Tessa continued for the next few minutes, telling Jenelle about her prom clothes, the group of friends she was going with, the limo they'd all chipped in for, and the song list she hoped the DJ was going to play. Jenelle relished Tessa's moment of normalcy.

Jenelle nodded her head, smiled, and thought to herself, *This girl is so cool and so much better, I wouldn't change what I do for the world.*

2
HIDING IN PLAIN SIGHT

RONALD BARNES

Note: The following chapter is based on actual events and the case files of an active law enforcement officer with over ten years of experience. The officer requested anonymity and is hereafter known as Detective Ronald Barnes.

PART 1, FEBRUARY 2017

"Happy birthday to you!" the party-goers sang the last verse to seven-year-old Maria as she blew out the candles and smiled.

Aunt Erlinda and her cousin Cassie were Maria's only family that lived nearby. Erlinda was a skilled baker and proudly made the chocolate birthday cake with a buttercream frosting dyed bright pink. She also brought shiny colored balloons that created a festive setting.

"What do you say?" Monique asked her daughter.

"Thank you, Aunt Erlinda!" Maria expressed with excitement and then eagerly asked, "Can we have the cake now?" Monique leaned over the table, smiled at her daughter, and cut the cake into slices. Erlinda snapped a few photos with her phone.

The birthday girl received her piece first and was also the first to finish. Then, with the innocence and excited enthusiasm that a seven-year-old child could get away with, she asked, "Is it time to open my presents?"

"As soon as everyone's done," her mother answered with a small joyous laugh. The crowd of a dozen people were quietly devouring their cake, and genuinely enjoying the Saturday afternoon birthday party.

Erlinda, Cassie, and Erlinda's new boyfriend, Carlo, felt relaxed and happy in the small house on Main Street in Broomfield, CO. Erlinda took several pictures of Maria with the balloons, friends, and family members to later be framed.

The small dining room couldn't fit the seven kids and five adults, so a few of the younger kids sat on the laps of a family member. In the center of the table was Maria, with several balloons attached to her chair. One of them was a silver star and Maria enjoyed holding the balloon close and seeing her slightly warped reflection. She laughed at herself and turned the balloon towards Cassie, who was sitting next to her. She looked at her own funny reflection and giggled like a child herself and casually flipped back her straight black hair. The fifteen-year-old teen was a short, pretty girl, and a younger replica of her mother.

Maria opened several other gifts, and the last one remaining was from Cassie. It was an envelope that contained a colored piece of paper. On it was written, "This coupon entitles Maria to get a manicure from her favorite cousin Cassie," in bright green ink. Cassie could not afford to pay for two manicures, but the teen could do a more than adequate job on her little cousin's fingernails.

"That sounds like fun," Monique replied.

"Can we do it now?" Maria asked.

"No silly, not while everyone's here. Besides, we still have games to play," her mother answered.

Cassie suggested, "We can set up an afternoon for the two of us. Would you like that?"

"Yes!" Maria squealed and then looked at her mother for approval. Monique nodded yes. Maria was itching to leave the table to play with her new toys.

"Actually, there's one more gift."

"There is?" Maria gushed.

"Yes, from me," Carlo answered and flashed a broad and easy smile, looking over the group and nodding his head up and down. His eyes returned to Erlinda and his smile appeared warm and content, as if everything were perfect in his world. He was a large man at 220 pounds and six feet tall, but he projected himself as a big teddy bear rather than tough or threatening.

Erlinda instinctually smiled back, her eyes sparkling with the excitement and strong feelings of her new relationship. Her reaction came easily because everything *was perfect*. She and Carlo were getting closer every day. He got along well with Erlinda's daughter, Cassie. Even Elinda's older sister Monique approved. And he enjoyed the family get-together, taking the opportunity to charm a seven-year-old girl at her birthday party. All eyes were on Carlo.

"You didn't have to do that," Monique told him.

"I wanted to, and I wouldn't have missed this party for anything. Thanks for including me in this special family occasion," he smoothly said. Once again, he flashed his easy smile towards Monique, showing off his pearly white teeth, which seemed to sparkle as brightly as his diamond stud earring. Everyone was put at ease.

Redirecting his attention back to the birthday girl, he asserted, "Your Aunt Erlinda has told me so much about you." Making eye contact with Maria, Carlo slowly stood up, reached into his front pocket, and pulled out a small, wrapped jewelry case.

"Whoa, what's this?" Maria asked and her eyes lit up.

"You'll have to open it to find out," he said in a playful tone. He put his hand out to show her the gift, and she immediately snatched it from him. Maria excitedly tore off the wrapping paper and opened the box, which contained a small gold necklace with a little dolphin charm.

"I love dolphins! How did you know?" Maria beamed excitedly and showed her mother and the rest of the party guests the necklace.

"That was very sweet, but it looks expensive," Monique replied with a combination of approval and concern. *Maybe Carlo spent a little too much money?*

"It's worth it for this special little girl's birthday. You're only seven once, right?" Carlo said without hesitation. His eye twinkled, and he had Maria mesmerized. "Do you want me to put it around your neck?"

"Oh yes!" Maria squealed and handed the necklace back to him. Slowly and carefully, Carlo unclasped the necklace and gently put it over Maria's head.

"What do you think, Mom?" Carlo asked Monique. She nodded in approval, surmising that Maria would enjoy the jewelry. It was a dolphin pendant, so it was age-appropriate.

In that moment, Erlinda dared to think that her relationship with Carlo could blossom into something special; something that would last. Erlinda's dating record was spotty, and her sister Monique could smell a loser from a mile away. Although this was only the third time that Monique met Carlo, she was comfortable around him and his easy-going personality.

When the party ended and they were leaving, Monique whispered into her sister's ear, "I think he's a keeper." Monique wasn't one to quickly approve of the men she dated, so Erlinda responded with an appreciative smile and nodded her head. Both sisters knew that Erlinda was falling in love.

* * *

Fifteen-year-old Cassie never knew her father because he left Erlinda before she was even born. Erlinda struggled to raise a daughter on her own and worked several waitressing jobs throughout Cassie's childhood. Even though they lived in a small rundown apartment complex for the past five years, Erlinda was a bit of a neat freak and kept the two-bedroom apartment clean and tidy.

Erlinda diligently paid her rent on time. She was continuously employed and valued by her manager. She was the type who showed up every day on time and worked hard. That work ethic helped her survive financially with a steady paycheck, regardless of how the local economy was doing. And at five foot two inches tall and 115 pounds, it didn't hurt that she had long, flowing curly dark hair to frame her attractive face and perfectly proportioned body.

Of course, some of the customers were merely flirting with her, but she liked to think they were being honest when the regulars were surprised to find out that she had a teenage daughter and was thirty-six years old.

She was not too thrilled to be closer to forty than thirty, but most people thought she was still in her late twenties, providing her a boost of confidence when she interacted with customers. With her warm personality, friendly nature, and desire to keep customers happy, she was the whole package, and her boss couldn't have been more pleased with her job performance.

Throughout the years, she dated a few of her friendly and flirty customers, but it never turned into a long-term relationship. She felt bad if Cassie became attached to one of her boyfriends, only to have the relationship fizzle out. It was hard enough for Erlinda to accept the breakups, but it was even worse when Cassie became hurt and disappointed.

As Cassie became a teenager, Erlinda limited her dating, resigned to the sadness that she'd never find a good stepfather for Cassie. After her last failed relationship over a year ago, she decided to give up the dating scene, that is, until she met Carlo.

She first saw Carlo in the most unlikely of places, in line at the DMV. He was behind her and started chatting her up. But it wasn't in a flirty or creepy stranger kind of way, but instead how he would talk to his older sister.

He didn't use any pickup lines or suggestive innuendo. He casually asked about her job, and he was familiar with the restaurant but admitted he hadn't visited the place in a few years. He inquired about her hobbies and how her teenage daughter was doing in school after she mentioned Cassie.

He didn't comment on her age or attractiveness. He didn't talk about himself at all, but instead probed with a gentle and genuine interest about Erlinda and what was going on in her life. It all seemed very innocent and casual, just avoiding boredom until finally reaching the DMV counter. The simple and friendly conversation put Erlinda at ease. Carlo didn't hint of anything more than his desire to kill time at a place where no one wanted to be.

He didn't ask her for her number or make any suggestion of getting together for a date. Not that she would have accepted a date, but in a small way she was disappointed. *Perhaps she was closer to forty than she thought.* Or maybe he wasn't attracted to an older woman. They were both eventually called up to the counter.

Carlo happened to be standing near his car, talking on his cell phone, when Erlinda walked out to the parking lot. He gave her a friendly head nod and continued his conversation, but then appeared to change his mind and quickly ended his call. Just when it seemed they were going to part ways, he approached her from a few parking spots away, and she momentarily hesitated to get into her car.

He nonchalantly suggested that they meet up sometime for a cup of coffee before her work shift. *It's just coffee*, she thought. She agreed and he entered her contact information into his phone. Carlo casually mentioned that he hadn't been to the DMV since he passed his driver's test ten years ago. That put him at only twenty-six years old.

Erlinda was flattered when she calculated their age difference. She fully believed that he was simply being courteous by asking for her phone number. Why would someone ten years her junior be interested in her? A full seven days passed before Carlo sent her a text.

Carlo was in no rush to develop a relationship with Erlinda, and when they met for coffee for the first time, he sensed that she was vulnerable enough for him to worm his way into her life. And more importantly, the more he inserted his way into her life, the more access he'd have to her teenage daughter. But then it struck him that a mother-daughter combination would be interesting to his boss Rico. It might be easy to control them by playing off their fears for each other.

* * *

2013 CNN & Money Magazine
Best Places to Live
Louisville, CO
Top 50 rank: 2
Population: 18,924

A two-time number one, Louisville comes in strong yet again. It's a great place to raise a family, with well-regarded schools and a safe community. Louisville's housing market has been on the rise since 2008, due to its place in the technology-rich Denver-Boulder corridor.

Locals say the work-life balance in Louisville is hard to beat. Come summer, residents can look forward to weekly events featuring food trucks from local restaurants, beer gardens, live music, and much more. Then there's the Colorado sunshine, 1,800 acres of open space, and, of course, the Rocky Mountains, just a twenty-minute drive away.

* * *

Rico ran a small sex trafficking operation, finding willing sex buyers from the upcoming suburb of Louisville, as well as nearby Lafayette, Broomfield, Superior, and Boulder. Carlo readily agreed to be Rico's right-hand man and recruiter two years ago after joining forces on several illegal drug and gun transactions. Profits from drug sales to local teens was one thing, but sex trafficking took their cash flow to a whole new level. Rico had a girl and one boy under his control and the money from selling their bodies was mind-blowing.

Carlo actively looked for desperate runaways or lonely kids lost in the foster care system. Like a mountain lion hunting its prey, he'd use his stealth tactics on the unsuspecting. His good looks and likable personality helped him target people alone and without a strong family support system.

He always wore nice designer label clothes, had short dark hair that was dyed blond on top, and frequently smelled of expensive cologne. He told Erlinda that he was the sales manager for Rico's company that supplied hardware to the local tech companies. He easily pulled off the part of a successful young man, someone on the rise.

Rico initially told Carlo not to bother pursuing Erlinda for it posed more risk compared to a helpless runaway. Carlo forgot about her, but then Rico pondered whether he could turn the family situation to his advantage. Carlo was instructed to continue his romantic pursuit.

While it's true that Erlinda had a family to turn to if she were in trouble, it was also true that she wouldn't want any harm to come to her daughter, sister, or niece. Rico now needed time to figure out a way to make Erlinda and Cassie much more vulnerable, and then terrorize them so ferociously that it would guarantee their silence and submission.

They continued dating and getting closer for the next six weeks after the birthday party. Carlo would happily accompany Erlinda and Cassie to any family function. He was getting in deep, and just as important, the family was starting to like him.

Carlo knew that Erlinda was developing deep feelings for him. Through spending time together, he was assessing her strengths and weaknesses. He made mental notes of every fear or vulnerability Erlinda directly or indirectly expressed. One of her fears was financial stability, especially with the ongoing expenses of raising a teen girl on her own.

Erlinda wanted to provide Cassie with the best childhood she could afford. But the needs of teen girls are expensive. They desire nice things, and they want to spend money on clothes and shoes and not look like the kid of a working-class single mom.

Any extra money went into Cassie's wardrobe or activities and Erlinda was happy to provide her daughter with something that she didn't grow up with. Although no one would say that Cassie dressed like a rich suburban kid, at least she had a wardrobe to fit in with her group of friends.

Erlinda wasn't the kind of mom who would impulsively run out and buy expensive clothes for her daughter at the drop of a hat. However, with careful shopping, finding things on sale, and gently used secondhand designer labels, Cassie looked the part of a typical teenage middle-class kid. Her method worked well for years, and they rarely got into a financial jam, but it did leave Erlinda with financial vulnerability.

Although Erlinda was assigned enough hours at work, it wasn't a high-paying job, so she struggled to save any money and typically lived paycheck to paycheck. Carlo had a multi-tiered strategy. Erlinda was about to have *the worst week of her life*.

* * *

Carlo recognized the first way to stress out Erlinda would be to get her fired. That wasn't going to be difficult because the restaurant owner was a frequent customer of Rico's. Fifty-two-year-old Kyle Mancini had a thing for young boys, and frequently went to purchase time with Rico's thirteen-year-old boy. The boy was a runaway and was completely under Rico's control for the past year, being kept at Rico's house most of the time. Rico provided an afternoon *freebie* to Kyle, and that's all it took for him to readily agree to end Erlinda's employment.

Carlo knew that Erlinda was a good waitress and could easily find another job. He had to make sure that she was pushed over a financial ledge.

"Can this week get any worse?" she remarked in an exasperated tone as she let Carlo into her apartment and rubbed her elbow. Someone had sneaked up behind her in the grocery store parking lot, punched her upper arm, and stole her purse. She had a severely bruised arm, and the thief got away with her identification and grocery cash for the week.

"I can't believe you got mugged and your car got stolen on the same day. I'm really sorry, baby," he said with sympathy. "Have the police said anything about either robbery?"

"No, I never saw the guy's face and it happened so fast. They don't have much to go on. I cancelled my debit card, but they got away with all my money."

"It's lucky you had your phone in your jeans."

"Yeah, but how am I going to look for a new job without a car? I still don't know why I was fired. I didn't do anything wrong, I don't think," she said with a loud sigh, clearly trying to deal with the stress. "There was one customer who didn't like his food, saying that his burger was overcooked and dry, but that's not my fault. Why would I get fired for that?"

"I don't know," Carlo commiserated and opened his arms for her to accept his embrace. "I can drive you places if you need help," he offered and gave her a loving hug.

"But the bigger problem is that I don't have any money for a new car. And with this elbow, I won't be able to hold a tray of food for at least a few weeks."

"Yes, you'll have to wait until that is fully healed."

"I should have never let my car insurance lapse. I was gonna get it renewed. I was planning on it, I swear, but I wanted to skip a few payments and save some money," Erlinda explained.

"I thought it was a good plan when you told me about it a few weeks ago. You would have renewed your insurance a month before your car registration was due and it wouldn't have been a problem," he said.

"That is, until somebody decided to steal my car. I couldn't come up with a down payment when I *had* a job, but now that's gone too . . ." Erlinda trailed off and started to cry. Carlo immediately stepped closer for another soft, consoling hug.

"It'll be okay, I promise," he encouraged.

"At least I still have you, don't I?"

"I'm right here, baby. I'll be your rock," he said to her, and turned his head to kiss her.

After the long kiss, Erlinda wiped a tear from her eye and told him, "I need you so much. You've been the best thing to come into my life in a long time. I think I . . ."

"You can say it baby because I feel the same," Carlo responded and beamed a smile.

"You do?"

"Yes, I love you," Carlo professed.

"You don't know how good it makes me feel to hear you say that."

"No one loves you like I do," Carlo emphasized.

"I haven't felt this way about anyone in a long time. I love you with all my heart," she replied, and they continued their long embrace.

"We've got an hour before Cassie is back from school," Carlo suggested with a raised eyebrow and looked towards her bedroom.

"Oh yeah, honey, I'm going to show you something special," Erlinda answered with a fun and mischievous smile.

"I like the way you're talking," Carlo enthusiastically responded.

1 HOUR LATER

Afterwards, Erlinda brought up the subject of her unemployment. "I think we should get dressed, and you can drive me to a few restaurants so I can fill out some job applications."

"I've got an idea that might help you," Carlo replied.

"You mean a loan?" she asked with hope.

"Something better than that. How about you and Cassie move in with me? You won't have to pay rent, and it'll give you some time to land on your feet. Plus, it'd be good for us, you know?"

"Oh, I never thought about that. Do you mean it?" she asked.

"Absolutely," he said, and his facial expression conveyed his level of seriousness. His normal jovial expression and tone were replaced with the anticipation of her decision. But his countenance didn't convey love, but instead how she'd expect him to negotiate an important business transaction. Erlinda quickly dismissed her perception.

"Well, it would really help me out," she answered with some hesitancy, pausing in thought for a second, and then continued, "and it's the next logical step in our relationship. You've got an extra bedroom for Cassie, right?"

"Of course, I just need to clean out the closet. It's almost the end of the month, so if we moved you over this weekend, you won't have to make another rent payment," Carlo pointed out.

"I don't have the money for it anyway, so yeah, that makes sense. I just want to run it by Cassie before making a final decision."

"Sure, I understand. This arrangement will help you save money for a car."

"Yeah, that's the last thing I feel like spending money on, but I don't have a lot of other choices," she conceded. *I have the perfect boyfriend,* she thought to herself.

"It's a great plan," he reassured her.

"You're my hero," she said and leaned up and kissed him passionately.

"I'll be your Superman. I'll take care of you and you can take care of me."

"That sounds fair," Erlinda concluded.

"You just relax, baby. You should take some time off before looking for work. You need a break."

"Do you think so?"

"Yeah, you deserve it. When was the last time you took some vacation time?" Carlo asked.

"It's been a while," Erlinda admitted.

"Besides, it will be harder to get a job with your hurt elbow. Let me pamper you for a while," Carlo suggested and she felt more relaxed.

This is going to work out perfectly, Carlo thought to himself. That weekend, Erlinda and Cassie moved in with Carlo. He had newer furniture, so they sold or gave away most of Erlinda's furniture. It was by design that Erlinda moved with few possessions, just a few suitcases of clothes and family mementos.

22 DAYS LATER

"Why are we going to a gentlemen's club?" Erlinda asked as they parked the car. They were in the nearby city of Boulder around 9:00 p.m.

"We're going to meet my boss, Rico. He's the owner of the club."

"I thought he owned the parts supply business," Erlinda replied.

"He owns this too," Carlo answered with a gruff tone, a man tired of being *Mr. Nice Guy.*

"Hmmm?" she asked in a hesitant and questioning manner.

"I got you a job," Carlo mentioned casually.

"Oh, waitressing?" she inquired.

"Not exactly. You need to bring in more money than that," he commanded in a stern tenor as they walked to the rear entrance door. Rico was waiting for them, and he escorted them into a small dressing room. There were two other women getting dressed and putting makeup on. When Rico walked in, Erlinda noticed their faces light up with fear.

"Scram!" Rico instructed, and without balking, the two women immediately stopped what they were doing and left the room.

"What's going on?" Erlinda asked.

"Here, put this on," Rico told her with unwavering authority, ignoring her question and handing her a child's size *Disney Princess* t-shirt.

"For what?" Erlinda asked and looked at Carlo for an explanation. Why didn't Carlo protest Rico's demands? He was stone-faced and she suddenly became stressed. Her stomach tightened up, trying to process his command.

"It's *'mom'* night at the club, and you're going to be the first contestant," Carlo stated without feeling.

"What?" Erlinda asked with shock and annoyance, "Oh, I don't think so."

"It's about time that you contribute to the household. You've been sitting around getting your nails and hair done, acting like the Queen of Louisville, and I've been paying for everything."

"But you told me to take a little vacation," Erlinda protested.

"Vacation's over," Carlo shot back with an unwavering facial expression. It was sinking in that this situation wasn't a joke, *so what's going on?*

Rico stared at Erlinda with his arms folded. His thin mustache curled around his lip to form a scraggly goatee. Twenty-nine-year-old Rico stood taller than Carlo but thirty pounds lighter with a wardrobe that screamed *gangster*.

"But . . ."

"How about I kick you and Cassie out on the street?" Carlo interrupted. "Is that what you really want? I've been taking care of you for weeks now. That wasn't for free, you owe money for that.

And I mean a lot of money." Carlo took a half step towards Erlinda, puffing his chest out to appear more menacing.

"I can get a job," she offered.

"Too late. You're going to make a payment, starting tonight. Do you hear me?" he asked without a smile. Erlinda couldn't understand his change of attitude.

He didn't wait for an answer and stepped in closer to Erlinda, and quickly placed his strong hands on the opening of her blouse. In one quick movement, he tore open her top, with the buttons flying everywhere. He spun her around and immediately removed the blouse.

Erlinda drew in a loud breath as Carlo unclasped her bra. She was shocked and embarrassed by the situation and tried to cover herself up, which generated a sinister laugh from Rico.

"Mama, I don't know what you're doing that for, since you're going to be on stage in five minutes showing it all to everyone," Rico commented.

Erlinda involuntarily shuddered and continued to protest, "I can't do that."

"That's fine, *that's just fine*," Rico stated, nodding his head up and down, and then raised his voice, "Carlo, go back to your apartment and find Cassie, and we'll make her dance up there instead."

"What? You can't do that, she's only fifteen."

"Do you think any of those guys in the audience are going to complain? Do you think anybody cares about helping *you*?" Rico taunted her.

"Go back to your apartment and throw out all her stuff into the street. You don't even have a crappy car to sleep in. There's a couple of cardboard boxes out in the alley. I'm sure Cassie would like that, don't you think?"

"I'll just go to my sister's," she countered, still brazen with anger.

"Do you think we're going to let you out of here, your debt unpaid?" Rico snarled.

Erlinda thought, *How could Carlo work for a man like this?* A thousand questions were going through her mind, none of them with good answers. There's no doubt that Rico was dangerous.

"You're not going anywhere," Carlo threatened and Erlinda noticed his fists were clenched. "You're going to put that little t-shirt on, get out there and you're going to smile at everyone in the audience so you make *me* some money. It's either you or Cassie."

"What? No, please don't," she begged. She wondered, *what has happened to my perfect boyfriend*?

"You're gonna be up there the rest of the night, doing the best to get their attention. You get up close enough so they can throw money at you. Do you understand?" Rico asked.

"Yeah, okay, maybe just this once," Erlinda submitted. It was then Erlinda decided that tomorrow she would call her sister for help.

"That's right, and so there's no doubt, when Rico gives you the signal, you take it all off," Carlo commanded and grabbed Erlinda's arm and walked her from the dressing room to the stage. He looked back and Rico gave him an approving wink.

THE NEXT DAY

"Check this out," Carlo remarked and turned Erlinda's phone around so she could see the video of her striptease at Rico's club. Carlo had taken her phone the previous night and hadn't given it back. They were sitting at the kitchen table and Cassie had already gone off to school. Carlo forwarded to the part when Erlinda was completely naked, and a drunk guy at the foot of the stage was hollering in delight.

"You filmed this?" she asked in disbelief.

"Of course. Your dancing was a little awkward, but you'll get better soon enough. You're going back tonight, and I've got big plans for you!"

"No, I'm not. I told you and Rico that it was only going to be that one time. Honey, what's happening?" she asked, pleading for a rational explanation. When was he going to declare that it was an elaborate prank?

"I'll tell you what's going on," he coldly responded. "It's about time that you start earning your keep. You've been lounging around here for weeks and you now owe me five grand."

"Five thousand dollars! What are you talking about?" she asked with total incredulity. Carlo silently stared at her. "Fine, I'll go out and look for a job today."

"Are you stupid? I've already found you a job working at Rico's club and that's where you're going."

"I've never seen you this way. You've never talked to me like this. I love you, Carlo. Why are you making me do this? Don't you love me?" she asked, visibly upset and gesturing for a hug from him.

"I guess you *are just stupid*," he responded with cruelty, pushed her away, and then said, "Now it's time for you to pay me back and stop complaining–unless, of course, you'd like Cassie to join you on stage tonight. Should I send this video to all your contacts and invite them to the show? I'm sure your sister and Cassie would love to see this video." He laughed loudly.

"You can't show her that!" Erlinda exclaimed, thoroughly embarrassed that Carlo had evidence of her striptease.

"I can *and I will*," he corrected in a belligerent manner.

Erlinda noticed his eyes were dark and intimidating. It was in that moment that Erlinda realized that their relationship was never going to return to what she cherished. She was dumbfounded and confused that the love of her life was treating her this way, and his personality had changed overnight. *Did she miss something? Were there signs that she didn't notice?*

Erlinda met Rico once before, and the word *snake* came to mind. But not Carlo, not her wonderful, sweet, and tender Carlo. She was devastated by the turn of her relationship. But how could she pay back five thousand when she didn't have any money to her name, didn't have a car or a job, and had a daughter to take care of? She immediately thought about going to her sister's place and staying there for a few days, but Carlo put an end to that with the next sentence out of his mouth.

"And don't think about going to Monique's. Trust me, you don't want her *and little Maria* involved with Rico," Carlo advised with sincere honesty, and Erlinda was too scared to ask why, but in her gut, she knew that the last thing she wanted was Rico coming after Maria.

In order to be convincing, Carlo briefly softened his tone, "Look baby, just work for Rico for a while. You'll pay off your debt, and everything can go back to the way it was before," Carlo implored and smiled back at her, and she momentarily saw the face she fell in love with.

"You're a good-looking woman, so I'm sure if you put a little more effort into it, you could get a lot of tips and pay back the five grand quickly. Maybe in just a week or two. And no one will ever know, I promise," Carlo encouraged.

Maybe, thought Erlinda. The best plan would be to get this debt paid, leave Carlo for good, and hide out at Monique's house. She'd take them in until Erlinda found a job. *Just a couple of weeks and then I'm out.*

"Well . . ." Erlinda said hesitantly.

"Do it for me, okay honey? We need to get this done so we can move past this," he said with all the reasonableness and calmness as if he were suggesting where to go for dinner. But there weren't any gentlemen at *this* gentlemen's club.

"Okay, but no more videos. You can't tell Cassie and you have to swear you're not going to show it to anybody."

"It'll be our secret. But I'm keeping your phone for now."

2 WEEKS LATER

"I don't think the threat of being exposed as a stripper is going to be enough," Carlo said and took a drag on his joint. "Each day I keep telling her that she's almost done paying off her debt. She thinks she'll be debt-free after tonight. She is so dumb; she bought every word of it. I don't think she's told Cassie and I've been holding onto her phone so I know she hasn't told anyone. I've been texting Monique, setting the stage for a fight between the two of them."

"Good. Now we need to push her over the edge," Rico barked back to Carlo as they were sitting in Rico's dingy office at the strip club, then his eyes lit up, and he stated, "I can't wait to get my hands on Cassie."

"You and me both."

"That girl is fine and is going to make us a lot of money."

"Are we set up for tomorrow night, Erlinda's private dance?" Carlo asked.

"Yeah, I've got one of the regulars that's interested in a dance and a whole lot more. He wants Erlinda and Cassie for two hours."

"That's a good start. Soon I'll be able to line up a bunch of willing buyers. I may need to knock her around a little bit because she isn't going to willingly let this guy have sex with her *and her daughter*," Carlo pointed out.

"Oh, you won't need to touch her. I'll take care of that."

"What do you mean?" Carlo inquired, a little confused.

"I'm gonna take care of one of my problem girls and replace her with Erlinda and Cassie. A two for one deal; I like that! I won't have to lay one little finger on her, but they'll do whatever we tell them. You just bring them over tonight," he said with evil glee.

LATER THAT EVENING

"I don't want to go to Rico's house tonight," Cassie said in a snotty teenage tone. "That guy gives me the creeps," she had easily concluded after meeting Rico once before. She noticed a transformation in Carlo who went from being her mom's near-perfect boyfriend to a cold and demanding asshole. She was regretting that they moved in with Carlo.

"I don't care what you want, you're going," Carlo commanded with full authority.

"You're giving me the creeps, too," Cassie quipped back.

She saw the back of his hand coming at her, but it didn't register that he was going to hit her. It was no longer a question once his hand landed on her cheek at full strength. The powerful blow knocked Cassie straight to the ground, and she didn't even have time to scream out in pain before she landed on the apartment floor with a thud.

"Stop!" Erlinda pleaded, shocked at the quick and vicious blow to her daughter. She took a step towards Cassie, but his menacing glare stopped her in her tracks, as if her shoes were stuck onto the floor with crazy glue.

"You should keep your daughter in line," he ordered. "We need to go to Rico's now."

"Mom?" Cassie asked, imploring her mother to protect her from Carlo. Cassie was still in shock that Carlo had struck her so fiercely and inflicted so much pain with just one slap. Her cheek was already starting to swell and it was bleeding a little from the cut caused by a ring on Carlo's finger.

"Just do what he says. This will be the last time, I promise," Erlinda replied in a trembling voice. It was now clear that their former loving relationship was completely over. She wanted her debt to finally be paid so she could move out of the apartment. They headed out and into Carlo's Cadillac Escalade. Ten minutes later, they were at Rico's tiny house in one of the more run-down sections of town.

The first thing Cassie noticed was that the place was dingy, dirty, and full of fast-food wrappers thrown about in random places. But the worst part about it *was the smell.* She couldn't quite figure out what it was. Could it be dusty, smokey, moldy, or food going bad? Had it been cleaned, *ever*? Cassie's simple description of Rico's house was that it was *gross.*

"This way," Rico instructed Erlinda and Cassie without so much as a friendly greeting. He grabbed both of their cellphones and then quickly ushered them into a bedroom with a not-so-gentle shove.

The small bedroom contained a full-size bed and a dresser, and Cassie noticed the room's only window was boarded up. It contained one small lamp, casting shadows throughout the room. The gloomy room increased the fear growing in the pit of Cassie's stomach. *Why would Rico board up the window?*

She casually walked towards the window to get a closer inspection. She tried tugging on one of the wooden boards, but it didn't budge. They were screwed in tight and blocked any outside light. There was no way out of that room and a sense of dread came over Cassie. The dread turned into panic when she heard the deadbolt close behind her. And then another one. And then another one.

Cassie turned around to look at the bedroom door and heard the last of the four deadbolts locking from the other side. Her fear level doubled. She desperately looked at her mother for some reassurance and comfort, but instead, it was like looking in a mirror. *Her mom's face was overflowing with fear.*

"Mom, what's going on?" Cassie asked with an unsteady voice.

"I don't know. I'm sorry I got you into this," Erlinda answered and started to cry.

"I'm scared. What are they going to do?" she asked and stepped towards her mother, and they embraced, trying to comfort one another, both hoping that the evening would magically get better.

Neither one had any idea that in exactly eighteen minutes, their lives would be changed forever.

* * *

You're only young but you're gonna die
I won't take no prisoners won't spare no lives
Nobody's putting up a fight
I got my bell I'm gonna take you to hell
"Hells Bells" - AC/DC

16 MINUTES LATER

Carlo used his large and powerful fist to punch Zoey between the eyes, knocking her out cold. "That felt good," Carlo commented in a sadistic manner.

"You hit her too hard. I just wanted her subdued, not unconscious," Rico scolded. "It doesn't matter, pick her up and bring her into the room with me," Rico instructed. Carlo put one powerful arm underneath Zoey's armpit and waited a few seconds while Rico undid the deadbolts and dragged her into the bedroom.

Cassie heard the locks open and shuddered. *What's going to happen next?* She was not expecting Carlo to drag another teen girl into the room. Cassie noticed that the girl looked to be about her age, with matted hair, wearing a Denver Broncos t-shirt and ripped jeans, but not the kind of designer jeans that come like that when you buy them at the store. She couldn't help but notice the girl's eye sockets were getting more swollen by the second.

"What did you do to her?" screamed Cassie in fright.

"This is Zoey. She's become more trouble than she's worth and not earning her keep. Yesterday we saw her talking to a cop," Rico stated. Erlinda and Cassie's eyes were glued on the girl still being propped up by Carlo, as Zoey was unable to stand on her feet by herself.

"I don't put up with snitches. There are consequences," Rico stated in a calm and brutally cold tone. "You don't want to cross me, do you?" Rico asked. Cassie and Erlinda were too frightened to even respond.

"When he asks you a question, you better answer!" Carlo screamed at them. Both Cassie and Erlinda recoiled from his outburst. They nodded their heads in unison as tears streamed down their cheeks, with fear overtaking their brain.

"I want you to understand, I mean *completely understand,* what happens when one of my girls doesn't do what I say or tries to talk to the cops," Rico stated. He looked at both of his captives, reached into his back pocket, and pulled out an eight-inch hunting knife.

Carlo was still holding up Zoey and she was just starting to regain consciousness. She let out a soft moan and Carlo then shifted his arm to hold Zoey up straighter.

With a demonic and merciless glint in his eye, Rico looked at Erlinda and then shifted his eyes to Cassie as they cringed with terror. He stared at her for the longest two seconds of Cassie's life.

He pointed the knife at the two of them, and Cassie expected Rico to cut her or her mother.

She never expected what happened next. Rico nodded his head, and with his eyes still locked on Cassie, he grabbed Zoey's chin, held her steady, and *slit her throat.* There was no hesitation.

Her body momentarily reacted to the brutal attack and then went limp as blood quickly drained out of Zoey's neck. Carlo then put both arms under Zoey's armpits and threw the body onto the bed. She bounced once on the bed, seemingly in slow motion, and landed on her back, her lifeless body limp.

Her gash was deep enough to allow the blood to flow, soaking the sheets and mattress. Cassie recoiled with horror, wailing to her helpless mother, who was too frightened to move.

"I know you're not going to tell anyone about this," Carlo stated without emotion.

"You're both going to work for me, starting tomorrow," Rico added.

Both men walked out of the door, and Cassie's eyes momentarily left Zoey's limp body, and she stared at the bedroom door. She heard the first deadbolt lock into place. And then the second. And then the third. And then the fourth. *And then there was only silence.*

3:00 A.M.

Cassie whispered, "I can't stop shaking." The only thing Erlinda could offer was to gently stroke Cassie's hair as she cradled into her mother's shoulder. The two of them sat on the floor in the corner of the room, trying not to notice the *dead body* on the bed. It was unclear whether it was scarier to be in the dark, or to have the light on and plainly see Rico's ruthless destruction. They chose to close their eyes.

Cassie said, "I have to pee."

"You'll have to hold it," instructed Erlinda, who had no idea how long she'd have to wait for relief. That only made Cassie's physical pain even worse. She could feel her heart beating loudly and rapidly, as if it were trying to escape from her rib cage. Her stomach hurt too and was in knots, masking any hunger pain she should be feeling.

Cassie's muscles ached from sitting in one position, scared to make a move, and trying to be as motionless as possible. That didn't help the situation. The silence only fueled their own fears, as they were expecting Carlo and Rico to burst in at any moment and inflict the same fate as Zoey's.

Cassie recoiled, knowing the blood pooled on the bedsheets was slowly drying. She'd never seen a dead body before, let alone one murdered in front of her, let alone sitting in the room with it only a few feet away.

Cassie's skin was on fire, and her muscles hurt from the constant trembling and shaking from the fear wracking her body. The room was warm and her mother's comfort was nowhere near enough.

The fear going through Erlinda's mind was even worse than what Cassie could imagine. Working at the strip club was going to be a cakewalk compared to what she knew was coming next. Cassie had no idea what Erlinda endured, humiliating herself by dancing naked in front of a bunch of strange men. And her fear was more intense because this time, Cassie wasn't going to be let off the hook. In fact, her greatest fear was that Cassie was going to get it worse.

THE NEXT DAY, 10:18 A.M.

The deadbolts were finally unlocked. "Did you have a good night sleep?" Rico asked sarcastically and laughed. Neither Erlinda nor Cassie answered.

"C-Can I go to the bathroom?" Erlinda stuttered. Cassie was unable to hold it and peed in her pants a few hours ago. Carlo was called over and he roughly took Erlinda towards the windowless bathroom.

"Make it quick," he told her and locked the door from the outside.

"Do you want your mom to live?" Rico asked, as he and Carlo entered the bedroom. Cassie simply nodded.

"Then you're going to do what you're told."

Cassie slowly nodded again, unable to even formulate words.

"I will cut up her face so bad if you even look at me funny. Do you get it?" he asked with his voice rising loudly and suddenly, causing Cassie to flinch. The words bounced off the walls of the small bedroom.

"Yes," she whispered.

"Bro, you owe me for this," Rico said to Carlo.

"Yeah, and I've been waiting months," Carlo answered and took Cassie out of the bedroom and threw her onto the dingy couch in the small living room so Erlinda would be able to hear her daughter struggle.

"Make it fast, since we gotta get rid of this body."

"Take off your clothes now," he commanded. Cassie stripped down to her bra and panties, "All of it," Carlo instructed. Cassie wasn't moving fast enough so Carlo punched her in the stomach and she doubled over and fell back onto the couch.

"Please, no!" Cassie screamed and Carlo unzipped his jeans.

"This is the only thing you're good for," Carlo declared and moved in. In the background, Cassie could hear Erlinda pounding on the bathroom door, begging Carlo to stop raping her daughter.

14 DAYS LATER

Rico laughed. "Your sister says she's sorry about fighting with you." He held up Erlinda's phone so she could see it better. It was early afternoon and both Erlinda and Cassie were dead tired from the lack of restful slumber, slumping at the kitchen table chairs.

"What fight? What have you told my sister?" Erlinda asked with concern.

"You've been arguing ever since you let it slip that you had an affair with her loser husband."

"But that's not true!" she corrected.

"It doesn't matter. Monique and her husband have been fighting ever since. You were pretty graphic in your texts about what you and her husband did!" Rico taunted. "You also told her that Maria is a little brat and Monique is a terrible Mom. You've been pretty mean," he tormented and couldn't help from laughing.

"How could you do that?"

"It was the perfect setup to tell her that you eloped with Carlo and moved to Florida." He chuckled with amusement. "Monique wants to stop fighting and talk it over, but apparently you've refused!" he read the text and then snickered sadistically again.

"You've told her to butt out of your life, accusing Monique of being jealous that you're having a great time. You *are* having a great time, aren't you?" he asked, and his face turned to stone. Erlinda put her head down and refused to look at Rico.

Cassie broke psychologically within twenty-four hours of first being raped by Carlo. She was constantly in a daze and sat in silence, barely listening to the words Rico said to her mother. When he finished talking, she piped up, "Can I have some breakfast?" She was solely focused on her immediate need for nourishment.

"Get some cereal," Rico told her and pointed to a kitchen cabinet. Cassie slowly got up from the table and found a box of sugary oats. She dared not ask for milk.

"You've got a few hours to clean up," Rico said to Cassie. "We've got a new buyer."

Cassie in her traumatized state responded with a blank stare. Her will to fight was long gone.

"This could be a regular customer, so you better look good, and be bubbly and perky. I got you a new outfit," he remarked and held up a plastic bag and threw it to her. Inside were a pair of shorts and a t-shirt two sizes too small with the Denver Rapids team logo. "He likes soccer girls," Rico commented and laughed at her.

"I'll be waiting outside the hotel room," Rico scowled and continued, "If you say anything to him, you know your mother's dead, right?"

"Yeah," was all Cassie could manage to say.

"Don't forget I know your Aunt Monique and where she lives. And of course, there's your little cousin, Maria. I should fetch her for some kiddie porn. That makes a lot of money, you know?" Rico asked with a believable threatening tone. This got both Cassie and Erlinda's immediate attention and both sat up a little straighter in their chair.

"I promise to look sexy. I swear I'll make the new guy happy," Cassie quickly pledged and thought, *Is this now my life? It's starting to hurt to live.*

"There is only one way in and out of that hotel room, so I will know when you leave. Don't even think about trying to escape, or I will kill your mom," Rico promised again.

"I'm not going anywhere, I mean it," Cassie answered.

"Where would you go? If you go to Monique's, you're all dead." It was easy to take his threats at face value.

"Nobody would want you. Besides, you're just a piece of trash now. You think some nice boy is going to want to take you to the prom?" Rico cruelly teased.

"I never said that," Cassie answered.

"If all goes well and our new buyer is happy with you, he's going to want you as his prom date, so maybe you'll get to dress up after all. You better make sure that he wants to see you again," Rico said, continuing to mentally torture her. Erlinda was powerless and sat at the table quietly crying.

"Stop your sniveling and take your daughter into the bedroom and get her pretty." Both left the table without saying a word.

4:10 P.M.

He lied to his boss about a late afternoon doctor's appointment, an excuse to leave work early. She was going to arrive in twenty minutes and that gave him almost two hours of lust-filled pleasure. He'd be finished and back home at his usual time, so no explanation was needed for his wife or children.

Forty-two-year-old Lawson Falloner was the customer service manager at a local technology company in Broomfield and has been married for eighteen years. His wife was a human resource manager at a local hospital. They had a fourteen-year-old daughter and an eleven-year-old son. Both did well enough in school and rarely got in serious trouble.

The Falloners were solid boring middle-class citizens. He was happy in his marriage and was involved with his kids' education and sports activities. Lawson was born and raised in Colorado and the family lived in a nice house in Louisville. From many perspectives, he had a pretty good suburban life and was normal from many outward appearances.

But there was one thing missing, and in his free time, his mind would wander to one specific *fantasy*. After perusing the local Craigslist and Backpage.com sites, he became intrigued by the personal ads. After a few more clicks, he found several ads for escort services. He was drawn to one picture in particular.

She looked like his daughter's best friend. She had similar features, but obviously, it wasn't the same person. *But, close enough.* His mind raced and he found himself constantly thinking about fourteen-year-old Britney. He couldn't get her out of his mind. She was his taboo distraction. He was always delighted when Britney would come over to the house to study with his daughter. If only he could afford to install a pool or hot tub in the backyard so Britney could be invited over. The thought of Britney in a bikini made his blood pump even faster.

The best part was when they played soccer. *Yes, Britney*, he thought, with those long legs and toned athletic body running up and down the field. He counted down the days until the next game. He couldn't take his eyes off her. How he wished he could somehow get her alone. He fantasized about Britney secretly being in love with him, and her finally admitting that she needed someone more mature than the high school boys.

He visited pornography sites, specifically looking for videos of girls in a soccer uniform having sex with a middle-aged man. He repeatedly watched content if the video had someone who looked like Britney.

Afterwards, he'd peruse the escort website and allow his mind to wander with the possibilities, imagining an out-of-town soccer tournament where Britney would pay him a late-night visit in his hotel room. Just the thought of that scene made him forget about everything else.

He fantasized about her knocking at his door, wearing her soccer uniform, looking flushed and sweaty. Britney would immediately complain about how immature high school boys were and what she really wanted, *no, really needed*, was an older man, and she'd beg for his attention.

He couldn't believe that finally, today was the day it was all going to come true. Britney was the forbidden fruit that was going to taste so sweet. He'd waited so very long to have his soccer girl. She would desperately beg for his attention and approval. *He'd be more than happy to oblige.* The whole scenario was described in detail in the text to the escort girl. She assured him that he'd get exactly what he asked for.

He then received a text from Rico that said, "I'm at the hotel. I'll be at your room in one minute." All correspondence on the texts were actually with Rico. Lawson started to sweat with lustful anticipation. Then there was a knock at the door.

"Britney, come in," Lawson said with a smile as he opened the door and stepped back from the doorway.

The adrenaline rush hit him fast and the reality almost overwhelmed him. His heart was pounding with anticipation of knowingly doing something dangerous. He felt thrilled when he realized that his wicked thoughts were going to come to fruition.

Lawson viewed the encounter as *safe*; it wasn't *actually* Britney. It was fake, make-believe, and not real. *I never tried to touch Britney*, he thought. *I'm not a bad guy*, he told himself and today was simply fulfilling a fantasy so he wouldn't have to give in to his impulse to touch Britney. That made it okay, right?

He didn't want to hurt Britney, or his wife, son, and daughter. This was better. *No one gets hurt this way*, he rationalized. In fact, he was helping this girl out, providing her with some income, he justified.

"Hi," Cassie replied with a forced smile good enough to pass as real. Lawson quickly and quietly closed the hotel door.

At least the hotel room is clean, Cassie thought to herself, trying to find something positive.

"How was the soccer game?" Lawson asked.

"We lost, and I need someone to make me feel better," Cassie answered and gave him a little pout. "Can you *please* help me?" Cassie continued and put her hands on her hips. It didn't take much acting ability to fulfill Lawson's expectations. He didn't waste any time as he drew Cassie close to him and planted a kiss on her lips.

That's when Cassie left the room. Not physically, but emotionally, mentally, and spiritually. She had to escape. It was the only way she could stay sane. Once a strange man started to touch her, Cassie turned numb and expressionless. It was too painful to even try to process what was happening. If she left the room mentally, maybe she wouldn't feel ashamed and dirty.

After the first couple of days of being sold for sex, she left the room so that she wouldn't remember much of the details. She thought about something else, *anything else.* Thoughts before the day that Carlo came into her life were welcomed. She missed school, her friends, and watching her favorite television shows. She even missed her mom complaining about her messy room. She missed everything about her old life, but most of all she missed the simple routine of being a normal teen.

She thought about when she was a little girl and would curl up on the couch with her mother watching a movie and eating popcorn. Those were good days. Those were the times when she felt safe and loved. *But those times were gone.*

Carlo told Cassie that she needed to look sexy for Lawson and all the other clients. He told her over and over again that her sex appeal was her only redeeming quality. *That* was her value, so she better make sure Lawson wanted her and paid attention to her.

So whatever Lawson suggested, Cassie returned a smile and nodded her head. Whatever he wanted to do, she agreed. Carlo told her that Lawson wanted to be wanted. He needed to be needed, and Carlo instructed her to play up those points, so every couple of minutes, she would reiterate how much she wanted and needed Lawson. *He believed every word of it for the next twenty-six weeks in a row.*

223 DAYS LATER, NOVEMBER 2017

"Do you know why we asked you to come in, Mr. Falloner?" asked Detective Ronald Barnes as he escorted Lawson into a small interview room.

"Not exactly. An officer came to my work and told me I might be a witness to a crime," Lawson answered honestly and continued, "How can I help?"

"What do you know about Rico?"

After a slight pause, Lawson answered, "I never heard of him. Who's that?"

"And how about Carlo?"

"I'm sorry, officer, I don't know who that is, either."

"It's detective, and most important of all, how about Cassie?"

"Noooo," he said with an elongated tone with genuine confusion.

"Rico was arrested yesterday for selling illegal guns, along with his sidekick Carlo. Your phone number was on his cellphone," Detective Barnes explained.

"I've never even shot a gun, let alone owned one. What are you talking about?" Lawson inquired, still confused.

"Uh-huh, I see you failed to mention Cassie."

"I don't know anyone named Cassie," Lawson responded.

"Oh, I think you're familiar with Cassie."

"Who?" Lawson asked.

"Do you have your phone?" the detective asked.

"Yes."

"Do you mind if I take a quick look?"

"Okay," Lawson reluctantly answered and handed it over. When Detective Barnes searched for Rico's phone number, nothing came up.

"I see you've deleted your texts with Rico. I'm sure our IT guys can find it. Nothing is ever permanently erased."

"I don't know this Rico person," Lawson said, trying to plead his case and being completely honest.

"I'm referring to all of your activity at the hotel. We confiscated Rico's phone after he was arrested, and there are hundreds of texts about your *dates* at the hotel."

"What?" he asked, fearing that Detective Barnes knew something.

"Britney's real name is Cassie. We know you met her all of those times."

"Oh, no," Lawson exclaimed when it hit him that the police had direct evidence. His stomach tightening with stress.

"Rico sent you a few pictures. Do you recognize this girl?" Detective Barnes asked and showed him a picture of Cassie in a sultry pose, wearing a soccer uniform.

"She told me she was eighteen," Lawson lied. "She said her name was Britney."

"I never said how old she was. She's fifteen *by the way*, about the same age as your daughter. But that was the point, wasn't it?" Detective Barnes accused with an unforgiving look on his face.

"It wasn't me–someone borrowed my phone," Lawson countered.

"Don't give me that bullshit. The desk clerk at the hotel recognized your picture. You've been meeting her there every week for months!"

"This is awful; I'm so embarrassed. It's not what you think it is."

"What do I think it is?" the detective asked. He couldn't wait to hear what lame excuse this guy was going to use. He'd been a detective for many years and heard every excuse in the book. He didn't expect Lawson to be that creative.

"I was just there to get to know the girl. You know, help her out and give her some money for food and stuff."

"Yeah, right, that's not what you wrote in your text messages back to Rico. They were pretty graphic and specific. You weren't helping her with her homework."

"Well, I . . ." Lawson trailed off, not knowing what to say, knowing his excuse *was* lame.

"This girl has a real name. Her name is Cassie, and she used to attend Monarch High School before Rico and Carlo got ahold of her."

"This has to be a mistake. I was just there to visit with her to talk," Lawson argued, knowing the detective was never going to believe him.

"We have evidence of over twenty-six sex assaults on a child. Do you know how much prison time comes with that?" Detective Barnes asked.

Lawson silently shook his head.

"You won't get out of prison until your daughter is a grandmother, that is if you live that long. Is that what you want?"

"No, I'm sorry. I'm so sorry," Lawson answered and started to physically shake and contorted his face. He couldn't argue the evidence any further. He wiped the tears from his eyes.

"You had sex with Cassie, a child, at least twenty-six times. Was it more than that? Are there others?" the detective asked.

"No, of course not," Lawson answered defensively. "I really thought she was over eighteen, the online ad said so."

"Ignorance is not an excuse, and don't lie to me. You didn't think about how old this girl was. I read those texts and know exactly what you did to her," the detective replied.

"I'm sorry," Lawson repeated.

"Do you think she wanted to do this? Rico and Carlo were forcing her. Do you think you were her only *date*?"

"I don't know," Lawson replied, cringing.

"You don't know, that's perfect. Did you have sex with her mom, too?" Detective Barnes asked with disdain.

"No! What are you talking about?" Lawson asked and recoiled. This conversation was getting worse by the minute.

"They coerced her mother into prostitution too. They were both forced to have sex with strangers multiple times a day. Do you know what that does to a child?"

Lawson squirmed in his seat.

"No, you don't know because you *don't care*. You only were thinking about your own perverse pleasure. Well, you'd care if you took home a sexually transmitted disease to your wife. I bet you weren't thinking about your wife when you were at the hotel room forcing Cassie to do disgusting acts with you," Detective Barnes chastised Lawson with genuine repulsion.

"I don't know," he repeated and wiped his runny nose with the back of his hand.

"Helping with money for food," the detective scoffed and continued, "Everything you gave her went back to her pimp, her captor. Do you understand that?" Detective Barnes asked.

Lawson didn't respond because he didn't have any good answers.

"Did you beat her up too?" Detective Barnes asked.

"No, I would never hurt her."

"You don't think *you've hurt her*? She's scarred for life. You hurt her emotionally. What about mentally? What do you think you've done to *her soul*?"

"I didn't think," Lawson cried. "I'm sorry."

"Yeah, that's right, you didn't think. You're only concerned with yourself. What you did to Cassie was one of the most selfish acts somebody could do."

"I'm sorry. I'll never do it again," Lawson offered.

"Don't say you're sorry to me," Detective Barnes told him.

"I can apologize to Cassie."

"No, you're not getting near her," the detective stated and paused. "Do you want to help her?"

"Yes, how can I help? I'll do anything," Lawson replied with a ray of hope.

"I need you to testify against Rico. I need you to confirm that you were on the other end of this text conversation. We can easily tie this phone to Rico and charge him with sex trafficking someone underage."

"Am I going to be arrested?"

"Maybe, but it'll go a long way if you help us build a case against Rico."

Detective Barnes knew that even if Cassie was willing to testify, many children that have been traumatized like her have a tough time identifying the sex buyer. She might be able to identify Lawson, but she also might be too scared to testify. But first, Detective Barnes needed to find Cassie and her mother.

"Okay, I think I can do that, but . . ." Lawson hesitated, trying to think how he could help the detective and keep it a secret.

"But what?"

"Please don't tell my wife."

LATER THAT EVENING

After work, Detective Barnes needed to blow off some steam. He jumped on his *Specialized* mountain bike and rode to the crushed gravel path of the Coal Creek Trail in Lafayette, which led him past Louisville, where he then jumped on the Boulder Creek trail system, heading towards his favorite park, Chautauqua. He locked up his bike and started running up the trail heading to the top of the first Flatiron peak. He didn't have enough time this evening to make it to the top, but it would be enough time to decompress.

After being a detective for eight years for the county, with a total of fourteen years in law enforcement, he was assigned to a federally funded task force focused on human trafficking. This group worked throughout the Interstate 25 corridor, from Ft. Collins in the north to Denver to Colorado Springs in the south.

Members of the task force typically partnered with local agencies for assistance. Working sex crimes exposed him to a whole new criminal element. Interacting daily with the worst that society had to offer, the brutal nature of the crime, and the broken individuals he encountered were stressful and mentally taxing.

Now came the difficulty of piecing everything together. After the arrest, members of the task force were alerted but when they got to Rico's house, it was empty. They quickly discerned that several other people were living there. The text messages on Rico's phone were detailed enough so that only a few of the sex buyers were needed to testify to make a solid case. But that would take time, effort, and a little bit of luck.

Stashed away, they found both Erlinda and Cassie's phones, along with Erlinda's driver's license and Cassie's school ID. They discovered evidence of an underage boy being sex trafficked by Rico and Carlo, but they didn't find anything that would identify him.

The detective needed to find all of them. Not so much to bolster up his case, but because they were all in imminent danger. Carlo and Rico both made bail and were back out on the streets.

So, where were Cassie and Erlinda? After his workout, he planned to check local women's shelters to see if they had sought refuge there.

Detective Barnes had a daughter and two sons, and in a few years, his daughter would be Cassie's age. He shuddered at the thought of his own daughter going through what Cassie must have experienced. He immediately felt fear for his family combined with anger for Rico and Carlo. He had to force himself to calm down and focus on his breathing tempo as he continued running uphill on the trail.

How does this happen? How safe are my kids? How safe are my friend's kids? It's all happening under the radar, hiding in plain sight, in nice suburban towns and neighborhoods.

He thought of his wife and thanked God for the support she provided, as well as other family members and close friends. He couldn't do this job alone. He also was thankful for his two brothers who were also in law enforcement. Officer Rusty Barnes, his baby brother, worked in the mountains of Buena Vista, CO, and his older brother, Officer Jesse Barnes, worked in Littleton, just south of Denver. The three men were close and frequently helped each other with the stress of being a police officer.

5:11 P.M.

When Erlinda and Cassie woke up this morning, they were surprised to find the house empty. They were expecting either Rico or Carlo to coordinate their *date* with a sex buyer from the night before, but it never happened. They fell asleep, fully expecting to be woken up in the middle of the night. The other trafficking victim in the house, Rudy, a thirteen-year-old boy, was driven to his *date* the previous evening but didn't return.

Normally, Rico and Carlo would bring him back to the house afterwards, but none of them returned because they were arrested for an illegal gun sale while the *date* was happening. Rico and Carlo spent the night in jail, so when morning came, Rudy was stranded at the hotel room. He eventually left and wandered the streets.

When early afternoon came, it was time to make a decision, but Erlinda and Cassie were frozen with fear of getting punished for not going on their *date* the night before, so they waited at the house. By early evening, with Rico and Carlo still not home, they mustered enough courage to leave.

"Why can't we go to the police?" Cassie pleaded with her mother while sitting at a bus stop.

"And be a snitch? Do you remember what happened to Zoey? I don't want that happening to us," Erlinda snapped, still in a state of fear.

"But at least if we went to the police, maybe they could protect us. Or Aunt Monique can come and help us."

"That's the last thing I want, Rico showing up at your Aunt Monique's house. I can't let anything happen to them. It's bad enough that I couldn't protect you," she said and started to cry.

"I know, Mom, but there was nothing you could do. I don't want them hurting you either," Cassie replied. "So, where are we going to go? Do you even have any money for the bus?"

"We need to get far away, and then we'll contact the police. I'm just gonna beg the bus driver to take us somewhere, *anywhere*." Cars continued to pass them in the calm twilight of the evening.

"Is that them up there?" Rico asked, pointing at two people sitting at the bus stop. Both were in the Escalade, with Carlo driving.

"I can't tell–it's almost dark. Yeah, I think that's them," Carlo answered and slowed the Escalade to a screeching stop.

Cassie and Erlinda looked at the black Escalade and froze in fear. Their worst nightmare had come true, Carlo and Rico were back. Rico quickly jumped out of the SUV and immediately grabbed Cassie, who started to flail her arms and legs, trying to escape his grasp. He opened the back door and threw her in, and she nicked her head on top of the door frame, which momentarily stunned her.

"Do you want your daughter to be all by herself?" Rico asked, his face full of an evil and a menacing grin. "Or do you want to get in and at least try to be a mom to her?"

"No, please don't!" Erlinda shouted and started to back away. Several cars passed them and none of them noticed what was happening.

"You have three seconds to decide. Either get in with your daughter or we're gone," he coldly told her, and she hesitated for a moment.

"Okay, I'm coming."

* * *

I told her "I'll take care o' you, you take care o' me"
You've gotta P I M P and all I want is the money
She was the perfect ho' but what do you know
The bitch tried to gag me
So, I had to kill her
One less bitch you gotta worry about
She's outta here and that's how it turns out
"One Less Bitch" - Niggaz Wit Attitudes

14 MINUTES LATER

Carlo arrived at the storage locker and turned off the SUV. He quickly unlocked the unit and opened the door. Rico grabbed Cassie and Erlinda and pushed them into the small unit, barely able to fit the four of them because there were several boxes in there.

"Please don't leave us locked up in here," Erlinda begged.

"Don't worry, we're not leaving you," Rico answered, which didn't make either of the females feel better.

"Get the money," Rico instructed Carlo. He went to a box marked "Christmas Decorations" and threw out the trinkets from the top part of the box and underneath was a bag containing $50,000.

"Please!" Erlinda screamed, "Let us go! We won't tell anyone, I promise." She wasn't sure what they were going to do next, but it was always more terrifying to imagine what they might do.

"You need to shut up. I'm getting tired of you!" Rico shouted in an instant rage, taking two steps towards Erlinda and putting his hands on her throat, and then he squeezed. *And squeezed harder.*

Erlinda made a muffled choking sound and her eyes started to bug out. Cassie instinctively went to help her mother, but Carlo quickly grabbed her shoulder and slammed her against the metal door.

After another fifteen seconds of powerful choking, Rico crushed Erlinda's windpipe and ruptured her arteries. Erlinda hardly made a sound. He let her slump to the ground, and within a few seconds, noticed that Erlinda urinated. Her bowels released their contents and Rico snarled his lips when he smelled her poop.

She was close to having a stroke and would likely die soon, but Rico wanted to quickly finish the job. He lifted his leg and with all his strength, he stomped it down on her neck, *ending Erlinda's life.* Cassie gasped in horror at Rico's violent act.

Rico next said, "We need to get out of here. We're going to have to set up shop somewhere else. *She's* still young enough to make us a lot of money."

"We'll be able to find more just like her," Carlo said confidently.

Rico guided Cassie back to the Escalade, opened the door, and shoved her in with Cassie's head hitting the armrest on the opposite door of the SUV. Rico then instructed Carlo, "You sit in the back seat and make sure she stays quiet."

"Sure thing, boss. Were are we off to?"

"We'll cruise around and see if we can find Rudy. If not, we'll be in Fort Collins in less than an hour."

PART 2, 17 MONTHS LATER, APRIL 2019

There was Brandon, the twelve-year-old boy that Trisha was eyeing for over a month. They both were in Mrs. Appletree's sixth-grade math class at Lincoln Middle School in Ft. Collins, CO. Although they didn't sit next to each other, eleven-and-three-quarters-year-old Trisha consistently managed to leave the classroom at the same time he did. She couldn't figure out why it took a whole two weeks before he finally noticed her.

Trisha innocently asked whether Brandon understood the homework assignment, and of course he did. He was one of the smartest kids in class. She planned this moment for weeks and conjured up enough courage to hint that she was having a tough time with the homework. She was hoping he'd take the bait. He didn't.

She was going to have to be direct to have any chance with Brandon before the school year was out and she certainly didn't want to wait until they were seventh graders in the next school year.

She dug for more courage and suggested that they meet during their free period to compare answers. He agreed, and they planned to meet the next day. Trisha wasn't faking because she was struggling with square root calculations, a perfect cover for her ulterior motive.

He was so cute, with his naturally curly brown hair and adorable face. He hadn't started his growth spurt, and they were about the same height. Brandon was the kid in class who was always raising his hand to answer the teacher's questions, *even the hard ones*. He was athletic and excelled on the school's basketball team. He was also nice, although not the most talkative kid in school. She knew in her heart all of this to be true. It didn't matter if they had barely talked the entire semester.

He was cute, smart, athletic, and wasn't stuck up, so what was not to like? Now she needed to find a way to get his attention. And Trisha needed to do it before some other girl got her hooks into him. In fact, Trisha was convinced that someone else would swoop in before she could charm him at the library. And that would be typical of Trisha's life, *never anyone's priority.*

Trisha wouldn't dare allow herself to think that Brandon liked her too. She never had a real boyfriend before, at least one that was near her age. *Those others don't count.*

They both had a free study period right before math class, the perfect time to review their homework assignment. She slowly strolled towards the library, and after entering, she saw him at a small table.

She sat down at the table to work on their homework, and Trisha did everything in her power to appear cute and personable with just a touch of *cool*. She wore her best clothes, which consisted of snug jeans and a tank top. She wondered if her best would be good enough.

She wasn't in the circle of the cliquey, trendy, or popular rich girls. She wasn't athletic enough to make the volleyball team where the rest of the cool girls mingled. She didn't have any talent for the theater group. She wasn't considered one of the *weird girls,* so at least she had that going for her. She had average looks, and didn't stand out at all or draw attention to herself, which of course is sometimes a good thing in middle school.

It was difficult for Trisha to make friends. She was with a new family now in a different area of town so she didn't previously know the other kids. She was a loner who didn't have a close group of friends to hang out with.

Approaching Brandon, even just for homework, was out of her comfort zone. But having a cute boy notice her and be with her in public was going to help her social profile, and maybe open doors for additional friends. She feared that she was just fooling herself. Why would Brandon want *her*? She thought about changing her name to Jane, so she could be known as *Plain Jane.*

She knew she was average in every way and considered backing out and telling him to forget about doing their homework together. But then he looked up at her. *He remembered!*

Maybe there was a glimmer of hope that Brandon would pay attention to her and *really notice her.* The final middle school dance of the year was coming up this Saturday. She had no wild dreams about him asking her to the dance. But if he was going and she was going, maybe they could meet up! The more she thought about Brandon, the more she subconsciously needed his affirmation. There was no better place than dancing in the middle of the gym for all her tween rivals to view.

While doing their homework, Trisha nonchalantly asked if Brandon was going to the dance. He nodded his head and said that he and his friends were going, but he wasn't planning to ask anyone specific. She responded by letting him know that she too was going with a group of her friends, even though the truth was that she was going by herself.

The conversation diverged from math to music. She mentioned that she liked "Please Me" by Cardi B and Bruno Mars. He liked that song too, to her amazement and good fortune. After completing another homework question, she told him that since they both liked that song, and if the DJ plays it, they should dance together on Saturday night. He shrugged his shoulders and agreed. She was going to make sure the song got on the playlist.

He wasn't excited or enthusiastic, but he didn't dismiss the idea. Sure, it wasn't a full vote of confidence, but instead, it was casual and non-committal, similar to how someone might answer a request at the dinner table to pass the butter. *Yeah, sure, here's the butter, whatever.*

They continued reviewing the homework assignment, but her mind veered, trying to figure out what his response meant. Trisha wondered, *Does he want to dance with me or not? Is he just saying that so I'll stop talking? Or is he saying it because he does want to dance with me, and he's simply being cool? Why are boys so confusing?*

They finished reviewing their homework with five minutes to spare before the period ended. Brandon started looking ahead at the next math chapter and seemed engrossed in it. *Why won't he keep talking? Was he shy? Was he bored with me? Do I need to work even harder to get his attention?* She didn't know what to do. Should *she* say something? But that could turn into a strange conversation with lots of awkward silence. *What does it all mean?*

Trisha didn't want him thinking she was some kind of *freaky girl*. It's better to be quiet and let him talk if he wants to talk. Luckily, Trisha was saved by the bell, as it indicated that fourth period was over and now it would be time to go to math class.

Trisha stood up, grabbed her book, put it in her backpack and was about to leave the library. Even if they didn't talk at all, she wanted to walk with Brandon to class. Side by side, walking to class where everyone would notice. *That would be kinda cool, right?* But he was still engrossed in the next chapter. What was so interesting about math?

She stood there behind him, uncomfortably waiting for him to get out of his chair so they could get to class. She was going to walk with him to math class one way or another, even if that made her late. She continued waiting for another excruciatingly long forty-five seconds. *Don't disappoint me–don't tell me to go away and walk to class on my own. Show me you are a little bit interested in me.*

"I guess we don't want to be late," he finally said and closed his math book.

"No, we don't," Trisha said in a fun way, flipped back her hair behind her ears, and told him, "Come on, Brandon, let's go." He finally put his book in the backpack, and they made it to class just in time.

FINALLY, IT WAS SATURDAY NIGHT

Trisha was dolled up in her one and only dress, which was second-hand but nice enough with its white background and floral print. She was pleased with her looks and had asked the DJ to play her favorite song, but that was four songs ago, so what's going on? She leaned against the wall of the gymnasium, and two songs later, she heard the start of "Please Me." That was their song! She squealed in delight, clapped her hands a few times and was practically jumping for joy. She thought it would never get played.

She'd been keeping an eye on Brandon, who was across the other side of the gym, talking to his friends. Trisha wished with all her might, *please make eye contact with me.* Her wish came true and she started walking towards him. To her delight, he started to approach her. They were going to have this dance!

A few seconds into the dance, Trisha started to worry about making awkward dance moves. She was trying to mimic the dancers in the song's video. Was this going to be a disaster? Was the DJ going to stop the music, point her out, and everybody laugh at her? But the music continued and she noticed that Brandon didn't have the smoothest moves and luckily, no one else around her looked great, either. It eased her mind a little that she wasn't a complete dork, internally breathing a sigh of relief.

Before she knew it, the song was over. She instantly became nervous and stressed, waiting for Brandon to either continue dancing, or walk back to his friends. She glowed inside when he kept dancing, so she too continued. Then they danced to another two songs. Trisha couldn't believe how well everything was going. When it ended, Brandon suggested they get something to drink and she readily agreed.

They each grabbed a soda and started walking further away from the dance floor where the music was a little less loud. They were walking physically close to each other, side by side, and their hands inadvertently bumped each other. Brandon didn't recoil or run away. But on the other hand, he didn't react at all. Maybe he didn't notice?

Trisha decided to make their hands bump again, this time on purpose, and she held her hand in midair long enough to place two fingers on his hand. He gently placed his thumb over her fingers, indicating his acceptance of her affection.

Any level of affection was pure joy for Trisha. They were hanging out at the end of the gym, near the exit doors, continuing the finger embrace. She looked directly at Brandon and moved her head ever so slightly closer. When Brandon didn't react with repulsion, she moved another half an inch closer. He seemed to have gotten the hint, and he also started moving his head closer to hers.

Were they going to embrace? Yes! They were nose to nose and his lips touched hers, a little sideways and not a perfectly planted kiss, but there was no doubt, it was a real kiss, Brandon's first. Her mind raced and thought, *I finally got him to like me!*

In her excitement and enthusiasm, she took the hand that wasn't still in the fingerhold with his and placed it on Brandon's crotch. She gently squeezed and rubbed up and down for a second or two. There was no mistaking what was happening from her perspective or Brandon's.

Trisha knew what men wanted. She also knew what physical reaction would occur. She expected him to place his hands on her, but he didn't.

"Whoa, what the . . ." he said with astonishment, took a step away from her, and immediately dropped his hand from hers.

It took a second to register with Trisha that Brandon didn't want her advances. *But how could that be? She knew what men liked.* And she was giving it to him and all he had to do in return was *like her.*

His eyebrows scrunched up and he made an awkward smile from his own confusion and surprise. He didn't know how to react when Trisha went beyond a kiss, for that was the last thing he expected. And then he nervously blurted out, "I gotta go."

She watched in horror as Brandon walked back to his group of friends, and then pointed back at her. She could read the lips of one of his friends say, "No way!" The boys started to laugh and she was emotionally crushed.

She thought to herself, *What's wrong with me?* Her face became flushed with embarrassment and inflicted shame, but also confusion. Why would Brandon react like that? No man had rejected her before. She knew that it would get around the school. She'd hear the snickers in the hallway and be called a *ho or a slut.*

She feared some of the teachers would inevitably find out, and what little social status she had would be wiped out. She became embarrassed as well as angered by the situation. She was angry with Brandon and at herself. She had to get out of this gymnasium and away from everyone. She quickly slammed down the exit door handle and was out in a flash, and started walking as fast and far away as possible.

* * *

They cry in the dark
So you can't see their tears
They hide in the light
So you can't see their fears
Forgive and forget
All the while
Love and pain become one and the same
In the eyes of a wounded child
"Hell is for Children" - Pat Benatar

* * *

It was the most publicly humiliating moment in her young life. She thought, *How did I get here?*

The memories flooded into her immature brain. Trisha had a difficult time growing up, being in the foster system since the age of three. She was on her fifth foster family over the past nine years. Her single mom was hooked on meth and spent the first few years of Trisha's life in and out of rehab, usually unsuccessful. Trisha's mom was arrested for trying to rob a convenience store and the courts had no choice but to put Trisha in a temporary foster home. That was nine years ago.

It was clear that her biological mother wasn't taking care of her, but that didn't mean Trisha was embraced by loving and caring foster parents, the kind of parents who took kids in because they were nurturing and not simply looking to cash a check.

Trisha bounced from home to home and found it hard to bond with the family members. She was continuously in survival mode and longing for love and attention. But there was constant fear in the background, never knowing when she would be whisked away to join another family.

Her situation worsened when she was nine years old. A neighbor would watch her and her other foster siblings until one of her foster parents came home. Sometimes, the babysitter's husband would visit. At first, she liked him because he would help with schoolwork or read stories to her while she sat on his lap. She liked the physical affection when he would cuddle and tickle her and make her laugh.

One time, his tickles didn't stop and roamed underneath her clothes. This was confusing for Trisha, but the man assured her that it was okay and would be *their secret*. He would touch himself while he touched her, and he explained that's how adults played. It seemed strange to Trisha, but there was no one there to dispute him, and she felt special because she was trusted with *their secret*.

He would hug her afterwards, and she liked *that* part. She'd let the man touch her as long as he would give her a warm loving hug afterwards, then it was all worth it. She didn't get a lot of hugs and affection from her foster parents. They also weren't home often enough to give it. When they were home, they were tired and had a funny smokey smell, and didn't want to be bothered with Trisha or any of her other foster siblings.

Trisha kept waiting for her real mom to find her, but she never did. One day, the police came to the house when her foster parents were absent for a couple of days and they found her a new place to live. She never saw the touchy hugger man again.

Then at age eleven, it started happening again. *So, maybe this was a normal situation for kids*, she thought. But this time it went further with her foster mom's brother. He liked to touch Trisha and made her touch him too. *It was weird and kinda gross*, she thought to herself, and she didn't like it. And there weren't any hugs afterwards, which saddened her.

Deep down, she knew it wasn't right, and she was feeling guilty and frequently became angry that no one was protecting her. She was sad more often, and being in a new school *again,* made it hard to make friends, which put her into frequent moments of profound loneliness.

The man sometimes gave her candy or occasionally a few dollars, so at least she got something for it. She started to see sexual acts as a way to gain affection, even as minimal as she was receiving. Songs, music videos, media outlets, and television shows reinforced that she was born to be a sexual creature. She'd seen other girls who had smart phones take tons of selfies with their lips pouted and posing in their underwear. *She could do that too*, she thought to herself.

She tried one of those poses for the man, and he quickly lavished her with praise. She was learning that being sexy would get her attention. He eagerly coaxed her to touch his private parts. *At least someone approved,* she thought, but Trisha continued to feel sad and dirty afterward. He made her keep it a secret too. She couldn't understand why keeping it a secret was so important. It didn't matter because she had no one to tell it to.

Pretty soon, it was happening daily, so it occurred hundreds of times before her twelfth birthday. The man said that he loved Trisha, and that made her happy, for she couldn't remember the last time any family member said that she was loved.

Even though it was supposed to be a secret, she let it slip to a teacher, and it piqued the teacher's interest, and she started asking lots of questions. Trisha got the impression that what she'd done was wrong, but she wasn't sure why.

Then one day, a social worker came and took her to a counselor to talk more about it. She didn't say much because she wanted to keep their secret. For the next week or so, her foster mom was nicer than usual, but that attention quickly faded away. She got tired of talking and answering questions about it and eventually the counseling session stopped. The case was closed and nothing changed. Her foster uncle continued the sexual abuse. Trisha never felt so alone and was becoming desperate for attention.

One time, she found a bottle of Jack Daniels in the house. She inadvertently sipped some and it tasted like fire, and she started to feel giddy and lightheaded. She choked down more. Her foster mom caught her drunk but was more upset that Trisha stole her whiskey rather than an eleven-year-old was drinking. She started drinking small amounts to see if she could get away with her behavior and rebel against her foster mom. But her foster mom never noticed. *Trisha was invisible.*

She couldn't even dare to think about desiring love, even though her heart cried out for love and attention. She had no idea what parental love was about. It was as rare as winning the lottery, and the only place she saw it was on television. The molestation by the two pedophiles started to reprogram her brain and robbed her childhood innocence.

She thought for sure she knew how to get Brandon to like her, and it completely backfired. Based on her limited experience, she thought that was all it would take, and she was willing to give it to him to get something for herself. But he didn't want her, and *the rejection hurt.*

She was so confused and angry about how the evening unfolded and desperately planned to avoid school where she'd have to face Brandon and anyone else he told.

Trisha continued her long and lonely walk, and ninety minutes later, she was on College Avenue, near the university. She saw a McDonald's, still had a few dollars in her pocket, and decided to get something to drink.

She sat at a booth wondering what to do next. She was holding back the tears, hoping that no one would notice her. Most of the young college students walked by, caught up in their own world, and never gave her a second thought. *She was invisible once again.* Trisha tried to look busy, which was hard to do since she didn't have anything to be busy with. She wished she had a phone so she could at least appear preoccupied with something important.

Her head was down, staring into the gray almost colorless table-top, when somebody came up to her and asked, "Are you all right?"

"Yeah, I'm fine," she said in a meek voice, barely looking up.

"Are you sure? You don't look fine. Do you mind if I sit down?" the man asked, and when she didn't answer after a few seconds, he sat across from her in the booth.

"Are you meeting some friends here?" he asked.

"No, I don't have any friends," she responded in a melancholy tone.

"Oh, come on, a nice pretty girl like you has to have lots of friends."

She thought, *You think I'm pretty?* And then the man said, "What about your parents? Are they picking you up?"

"Yeah, right! Like they care about what I'm doing," Trisha exclaimed, looked up, and noticed the concerned expression on the man's face.

"What do you mean?" he asked with genuine interest.

"They never care what I'm doing, good or bad. One time I received an A-plus on a report in history class. I worked so hard on that report! I came home to tell my foster mom, and do you know what she said?"

"What?"

"Go clean the dishes. She acted like she didn't even hear me," Trisha explained and became visibly upset and wiped a tear from her eye. "They won't even know if I'm gone," she stated.

"I had foster parents like that when I was growing up, that is, when they were around. I never knew my dad," the man stated truthfully.

"I don't know my dad either."

"Your parents are idiots, aren't they? Some people are just bad parents."

"They're foster parents; I'm still waiting for my real mom to come and get me, but I don't think she knows where I am."

"Well, maybe I can help you with that," he offered.

"You can do that?" Trisha asked, perking up at the possibility of finding her real mom.

"I'm good with a computer. And we can search around for any records of her, especially on social media like Facebook or Instagram. I do that all the time."

"You do? I don't know how to do that."

"Your foster parents aren't trying to help you?" he inquired in a fake surprised manner.

"No. They're not doing anything. They don't care and there are four other kids in the house, so I'm sure they're too busy to help me look for my real mom."

"You don't want to go home, do you?"

"Why would I? They probably won't even notice."

"It sounds like your situation at home is awful. It must be difficult living in a place that you're not wanted, and no one is taking care of you."

"It sucks," she retorted.

"You know, I had a crappy home life when I was a kid, so I know what it's like. When I was your age, I just wanted one thing."

"What's that?" Trisha asked, fully engaged in the conversation.

"Someone to take care of me, someone who wanted me around," he calmly relayed and then asked, "Are you hungry?"

"Starving, actually," she answered.

"I came in to get some dinner for my boss and some of the kids living at his house. Why don't I get an extra burger and you can hang out with us? What do you think?"

"I don't know."

"You can eat your burger, and we can talk, and I can help you look for your mom tomorrow. You'll have to sleep on the couch though, I hope that's okay with you."

"I don't care," she said with growing excitement. *This could be a great adventure,* she thought.

"You wait here and I'll get in line for the food."

Trisha understood that going home would mean facing the reality of her life and everything in it. The first thing she'd see in her room would be her schoolbooks, which of course would remind her of the dance and what was going to happen on Monday.

The last thing she wanted was to be back in school, be humiliated, and have every kid talking about her. She certainly wasn't going to get any help from her foster parents. Being teased in the hallways would be bad enough, but how could she face Brandon? It would be a reminder of her *complete and absolute rejection.*

But then again, she wondered, *Who is this random guy at McDonald's?* He appeared nice enough and cared about what was going on in her life. He understood her and couldn't be any worse than some of the other families she lived with, she reasoned.

She didn't want to go home and receive any attention from her foster uncle. Besides, maybe it'd be good to make them worry and wonder where she was and see if they cared at all.

He returned to her table with two large bags of food, and Trisha's mouth started watering. She looked up at the man and said, "That smells good."

"Young lady, I never did get your name," the man asked gently.

"I'm Trisha."

"He extended his hand to shake hers with the enthusiasm of greeting his best friend. He smiled broadly and she immediately noticed his pearly white teeth as he introduced himself, "I'm Carlo." He motioned her to get up and follow him, which she did.

PART 3, 6 MONTHS LATER, OCTOBER 2019

"I think it's worth it to cut him in," Carlo stated.

"Yeah, I think you're right; there are too many prying eyes in the neighborhood. We can still do some volume at the house, but it's less risky if we mix it up and occasionally use hotel rooms," Rico concluded, paused, and then added, "We need a separate room to do our other business."

"If our operation expands, we're going to need an extra hand, and Jay could be a valuable addition," Carlo replied.

"I know his brother, but I don't know him at all. If it works, then maybe we can do some business together. Why don't you test it out? Book us five hotel rooms, and let's see what happens."

Rico and Carlo had outstanding warrants after they never showed up for their court appearance related to their arrest for illegal gun sales in Louisville. They set up in Ft. Collins, operating under the radar and selling Cassie for sex.

Trisha was immediately trafficked. Two weeks later, Carlo found Rudy homeless at the Pearl Street mall in Boulder. That area was a lucrative hunting ground for Carlo. A few months later, he found a new girl, Maureen, a fourteen-year-old runaway, already addicted to meth.

Organizing the appointments and travel to sell the bodies of four kids was keeping Carlo busy, whereas Rico was now handling most of the drug and gun business. Jay's street and computer smarts impressed Rico and could help expand their business. There was a lot going on.

Jay even looked the part of an awkward twenty-something computer nerd. He came to the small, rented house, and they went online and booked five rooms for Thursday through Tuesday at a nice hotel on Harmony Road in Ft. Collins. It was a step up from dingy motels. They expected the better location to attract people visiting the area for business.

Ft. Collins was booming economically, and the hotels were typically full or near capacity. Many of the local hotels held business meetings in their conference rooms, so it was the perfect place to set up shop for a few days; it wasn't unusual for somebody to book several rooms for multiple nights.

Carlo booked a room each for Cassie, Trisha, Rudy, and Maureen. The fifth room would be for Rico, Carlo, and Jay to coordinate the activities and organize their other business, primarily dealing drugs and illegal guns. Jay also had experience with creating counterfeit money, which they would use to buy gift cards at Target and other retailers. Rico was extremely interested to see the production firsthand and wanted to personally inspect the workmanship quality of the bills.

Rico agreed to give their new business associate a cut of the action. That is, if the promotional code worked in the hotel reservation system. Jay had worked at the hotel previously and the manager relied on him as the local expert for the hotel's software reservation system.

Jay discovered a little-known promotional code that would not process the credit card until the last evening of the reservation. This would allow Rico and Carlo to leave the hotel a day early and use a fake credit card number. They would be long gone before the reservation system flagged the card as invalid. Rico would never incur any expense.

Even more lucrative was that this reservation software was used by many major hotel chains, so they could use it all over the area and in different hotels under different phony names. It was almost too good to be true, but this time, it was true. If they ever were caught, they could use a real credit card and the police would never be called. It was a brilliant plan.

It was Jay's job to take Cassie to Planned Parenthood on Shields Street in Ft. Collins to get her second abortion. Cassie was not on birth control when Rico initially forced her into sexual slavery. With the volume of *dates* that Carlo immediately sold her for, Cassie was pregnant in the first month. She was about three months along by the time Carlo figured it out.

Cassie had no choice in the matter, and Carlo forced her into getting an abortion regardless of what she wanted. Cassie was issued birth control pills, and she took them regularly, but over the years, she was so mentally checked out that she typically skipped several days per cycle. Carlo noticed something different about her, and it was this morning that Carlo made her take a pregnancy test. It was positive.

He made the decision not to bother Rico with the details of her pregnancy. Carlo knew what Rico would decide, so he delegated the simple task to their new associate. Jay would take her to the facility this afternoon and set up the abortion procedure for next week, after their long weekend in the hotel room.

Cassie had mixed feelings about being pregnant once again. She had no idea who the biological father was, and she would never be able to figure that out. But deep inside, her maternal instincts were kicking in and she was desperately trying to think of a way to bring the baby to term.

She wouldn't be able to hide her pregnancy from Rico, and she didn't want to abort her child, so she had limited options. Over the time of her captivity, she never allowed herself to think too hard about escaping her situation.

Her mother was murdered in front of her, and she had no doubt that Rico and Carlo would follow through on their threats to harm Monique and her little cousin, Maria. There weren't many times when she was left alone long enough to contemplate an escape attempt. But perhaps the chance to save her child would give her courage.

She wouldn't be able to escape over the four days spent in the hotel room, but maybe there would be some downtime before her appointment at Planned Parenthood. Perhaps she could seize an opportunity. But for it to be successful, she would have to devise a plan beyond simply running away.

THURSDAY, 5:55 P.M.

Ding, went Carlo's phone. It was Cassie's first sex buyer of the evening, *the first of seven*. He quickly texted the guy to meet him at the hotel's side entrance. He walked downstairs, let the guy in, and escorted him to Cassie's room. He expected Trisha's buyer to be there in another twenty minutes. Jay was coordinating Rudy and Maureen's buyers. They were going to be busy all night.

5:58 p.m. Sex buyer #1: A 49-year-old male rapes Cassie, and she wished for it to be over quickly.

6:44 p.m. Sex buyer #2: A 22-year-old male rapes Cassie. The only thing she remembers is that he smelled bad.

8:08 p.m. Sex buyer #3: A 38-year-old male and a 43-year-old female rape Cassie. She remembers them being too rough.

9:13 p.m. Sex buyer #4: Three males, 19, 22, and 28-years-old, rape Cassie. She remembers them calling her vile names, and they spat on her when it was over.

10:33 p.m. Sex buyer #5: Two females, 29 and 33-years-old, rape Cassie. They told her that she needed punishment. She believed them.

11:58 p.m. Sex buyer #6: A 31-year-old male transvestite rapes Cassie. She was glad that this rape was quick.

1:24 a.m. Sex buyer #7: A 61-year-old male rapes Cassie. *Finally, the evening was over.*

The cycle repeated with nine more on Friday, twelve more on Saturday, and eight more on Sunday.

* * *

> Down with the swing (can't trust these hoes)
> I'm hangin' with Death Row like it ain't no thing
> I say you know can't deal (bitches ain't shit)
> > *"Bitches Ain't Shit" - Dr. Dre featuring*
> > *Snoop Dogg, Dat Nigga Daz, Kurupt & Jewel*

MONDAY, 7:23 P.M.

One of Cassie's sex buyers on Saturday accidentally left a flip phone. He used an old phone solely for arranging *dates* with girls like Cassie, instead of his regular smartphone. Cassie hoped he wouldn't contact Carlo or Rico and ask them about it, but she guessed it was more likely the buyer would simply get another anonymous phone.

Cassie stared at the phone, which had 50 percent battery life. She was in the bedroom that she shared with Maureen, Rudy, and Trisha. The room had two double beds, and at the time, Trisha was in the bedroom with her.

She stared at the phone contemplating what to do. Should she call the police? Should she call social services? Should she try to leave the house and then make the phone call?

Trisha noticed and asked, "Where did you get that?"

"Shush, quiet. One of the guys accidentally left it in the hotel room, so I grabbed it," she worriedly answered, knowing Rico wouldn't allow any of his captives access to electronic devices.

"What are you going to do with it?" Trisha asked.

"I said be quiet," she hissed in a loud whisper. "Damn, my message didn't go through."

"Who are you trying to text?" Trisha asked, but still not in a lowered voice.

"If I tell you a secret, will you stop talking about it?" Trisha nodded in silence. "I'm trying to get in touch with my Aunt Monique. She can come and get me and figure out what to do next."

"That will piss off Rico, and I don't want any of that!" Trisha responded, knowing that she needed to stay on Rico and Carlo's good side.

"I know, but I can't remember her phone number. It was programmed in my old phone, but I don't have it. I'm not getting the numbers right, and these old flip phones are so weird to use! Maybe this number will work," Cassie said and tried sending another text.

"Ahhhh!" Trisha screamed in a high-pitched voice. It was a snap decision to yell. She needed to score some points.

For a few seconds, nothing happened, but then both Carlo and Rico burst into the bedroom. They were surprised to hear screaming when it was just the two of them in the room. Sometimes, if a sex buyer was in there, there could be screaming. They were expecting the girls to be fighting. As she heard them approach the door, Cassie closed the flip phone and put it in her back pocket.

"What's going on in here?" Carlo demanded.

Cassie was sitting on the floor and Trisha was propped up on the bed, not near each other, so Carlo was dumbfounded as to what was happening. They obviously weren't beating each other up. Neither one said anything.

"I asked you two a question," he ordered, eyeing their guilty expressions. Rico was about to slap Trisha, who was closest, which motivated her to speak up.

"Cassie has a phone and is trying to call Monique, her aunt or someone," Trisha blurted out. Cassie opened her mouth slightly from the shock of Trisha's betrayal.

"Is that true?" Rico growled. Without waiting for an answer, he stepped over to Cassie, checked her pockets, and found the flip phone.

He calmly looked back at Trisha, smiled, and said, "Carlo, I want you to take Trisha out for some new clothes and makeup over the weekend. Take her to lunch and get her hair done. Whatever she wants."

"Sure thing, boss. She's earned it," Carlo answered and Trisha smiled faintly.

Rico flipped open the phone and saw that Cassie sent three messages to her aunt Monique, but they were returned as "undeliverable." The fact that she had failed to contact her aunt wasn't going to alleviate her punishment.

"I've had it with this washed-up whore," Rico coldly explained. He grabbed Cassie by the arm and yanked her out of the bedroom, into the kitchen, and through the door to the backyard porch. There were two cement steps from the porch to a small patio.

"I'm sorry!" Cassie cried out in desperation. "I didn't mean it."

"Do you think I'm stupid?" Rico barked at her. He was still holding her arm with one hand and with the other hand, he slapped her across the face with all his strength. Cassie was flung off the steps of the porch and fell onto the patio.

"Nobody betrays me like this!" Rico screamed in rage and added, "Don't you remember what happened to your mother?" By this time, Trisha, Rudy, and Maureen were near the back door seeing what the commotion was all about.

Rico was enraged that Cassie would dare defy him, dare to try to leave him and take money out of his pocket, and dare to disobey any of his commands. Cassie was woozy from the blow inflicted by Rico, but that wasn't nearly enough.

"Carlo, pick her up and put her face on that step, this girl is going to get *curb stomped*," Rico instructed with fury.

"Are you sure? She makes a lot of money for us,"

"She's easily replaceable," Rico answered. Carlo immediately did as instructed, not daring to point out that it might get noticed by a neighbor.

Cassie was trying to determine what happened and where she was. She immediately recognized the pain in her scraped knee when she fell down the concrete step onto the patio. Carlo repositioned her so she was face down on the edge of the lower concrete step.

Rico went up behind her, paused, and noticed that everyone was watching, which is exactly what he wanted, and he lifted his right leg. He slightly leaned forward and slammed his foot down on the back of Cassie's head and upper neck. The full force instantly inflicted intense and sharp pain, so severe that Cassie couldn't process what was happening.

The energy generated from Rico's body weight and strength immediately broke thirteen of Cassie's teeth, broke her nose and jaw, crushed her sinus cavity, and shattered her face in several places. The attack was so ferocious and intense that her brain started bleeding into her mouth, nose, and throat.

"Who's gonna want you now that you're ugly and used up?" Rico asked in the cruelest way. Rico had no plan of getting her any medical attention, and there was zero chance of Cassie ever recovering or resembling the innocent beauty that she once possessed.

She would never be able to speak normally again.

She would never be able to see normally again.

She would never be able to chew her food normally again.

She would never be able to breathe normally through her nose.

Her brain would never be the same, and she would never have the same cognitive ability.

She would never exhibit a pretty smile during a rare moment of joy or laughter.

She would never be able to hold her head up straight.

She would no longer be pretty.

She would always have a deformed face.

But none of that mattered because, within a minute of the assault, the life was draining out of her. Her future was shrinking and her human potential evaporated. Her energy was dissipating and her mind filled with *overwhelming despair*.

"Well, we have one less bitch," Rico snarled, and he looked at Carlo and said, "Take out the trash," and Rico walked back into the house. No one said a word, *and the silence was deafening.*

Cassie's brain could barely process thoughts. It felt dreamlike. *I need my mommy*, she thought. I need to have her cradle me in her arms and tell me the words that every child needs to hear, that *mommy will make it better.* Her final thought was, *Mommy, I'm coming home.*

At 7:36 p.m. on October 14, 2019, seventeen-year-old Cassie Anne Moore's life ended.

At 7:37 p.m. on October 14, 2019, Cassie's eleven-week-old unborn baby's heart stopped beating.

TUESDAY

"Are you ready to go?" asked Detective Elaine Korek.

"Yes," answered Detective Ronald Barnes.

Forty-two-year-old Elaine Korek was promoted to detective five years ago and was in law enforcement for a total of seventeen years. She was a short but tenacious woman and the mother of two sons. Detective Korek was a member of the Ft. Collins Police Department and was assigned to the case after someone called in a tip that morning.

After months of noticing strange behavior at a neighbor's house, a woman called the police department to say that she kept seeing young teens at the house during the day who never seemed to attend school. Of course, they could be homeschooled, but the woman indicated that the adults in the house seemed a little shady. Also, the men didn't look old enough to have teenage kids of their own and they had all kinds of strange visitors both day and night.

But what pushed her to finally make the phone call in the morning was hearing an altercation outside the night before, and it sounded like a teenager was getting beat up. The neighbor couldn't quite see what was going on in the backyard and waited until morning to inform the police.

Not only had the alleged assault on a child caught the attention of the police department, but so too did the fact that kids were living in the house, not going to school, and a bunch of strangers coming in and out of the house at late hours.

Detective Korek suspected that the case could involve human trafficking, and she contacted Detective Barnes of the task force. If it were something else, like illegal drug sales, Detective Korek and others in Ft. Collins Police Department would handle the investigation. The detectives headed to the residence.

Both detectives were in regular street clothes and parked several houses away to observe the residence and neighborhood activity. It was after lunchtime, and the house was quiet. After waiting for over an hour, they came up with a plan to check out the situation. They exited the car and approached the house, hoping that someone was home.

"Hello, I'm Detective Barnes, and this is my associate Detective Korek," he introduced them and flashed his badge when the man opened the front door.

"What do you want, officer?" Jay cautiously asked with a bit of visible nervous tension.

"Is that your car over there?" Detective Barnes asked, referring to Jay's 2014 Dodge Charger parked in the driveway. The officers previously ran the plates and knew that it belonged to a Mr. Jay Michael Coghill.

"Yeah, that's mine. Did I forget to pay a parking ticket or something?" Jay asked, still confused as to why the officers were at the house.

"No, it's nothing like that," Detective Barnes laughed, trying to put the man at ease. "It's routine; we received a report that a car like this was in an accident. Can you come outside and take a look at your car for damage?"

"Okay," Jay answered. They looked around the vehicle to see if there was any damage to the five-year-old Dodge, and as expected, it had a few minor scratches on the bumper.

"We were told that the driver of the car was a young female. Did you let anyone else drive your car?" asked Detective Barnes.

"No, of course not," Jay quickly responded.

"Do you have your driver's license?"

"Yeah, my wallet is in the house," Jay answered and walked back inside to retrieve it while the officers stood just outside the doorway. As he opened the door, Detective Korek noticed Trisha playing a video game inside the house. Jay was alone in the house with Trisha.

"A witness said the driver looked underage," Detective Barnes stated.

"Hey, that girl fits the description of the driver that got into the accident. We need to ask her some questions," Detective Korek told him. Jay appeared surprised and annoyed.

"I'm telling you, she didn't drive my car," Jay appealed.

"We still need to talk to her. It will only take a minute," the detective promised.

"Okay, but let's do it outside," Jay gave in and motioned for Trisha to come to the doorway. He gave her a serious stare, communicating to her to say as little as possible to the police.

"Hello, what's your name?" Detective Korek asked.

"Trisha," she meekly answered.

"Tell these nice officers whether you ever drove my car," Jay instructed in as nice and calm of a tone as he could muster.

"No. I don't know how to drive a car, except on a video game," she said and pointed back towards the house.

"All right, thanks," Detective Barnes stated.

"She looks sick; has this girl been to a doctor lately?" Detective Korek asked, looking at Trisha who appeared scrawny and mal-nourished. Her hair was uncombed and her clothes appeared dirty and ragged.

"Yeah, in fact, she went to a clinic last week. She's fine," Jay rebutted, pleased with the luck that he could truthfully tell the detectives about her visit to the doctor.

"Do you happen to have a receipt for that? Then we can be on our way," Detective Barnes asserted.

"Yeah, wait out here," Jay answered, annoyed that he couldn't get rid of them so easily. He went back inside, leaving Trisha with Detective Korek, who was talking and slowly walking away from the house.

Jay returned and handed the detective the statement. He scanned it quickly and then noticed at the bottom where the girl was checked for sexually transmitted diseases, and she had tested positive for syphilis and was prescribed medicine.

Detective Barnes stepped away for a moment and sent a quick text to a Ft. Collins Police Department patrol car parked around the corner. They had already determined that Jay was wanted for an outstanding parole violation. The Ft. Collins police arrived and arrested Jay. He didn't put up a fight.

The detectives found no one else in the house, and Trisha was too young to be left alone. This set up the perfect opportunity for the detectives to talk to Trisha.

"How old are you?" Detective Korek asked.

"Twelve, almost thirteen," Trisha answered.

"That's young to have a tattoo. What is it?" Detective Barnes asked, noticing her ink.

"A gorilla, I guess. Rico had all us kids get one," Trisha said, as if getting branded by a pimp were the most normal thing in the world. When Trisha told of more kids with the same tattoo, it was picked up by the detectives.

"When did you get it?"

"A couple of months ago, I guess."

"Do you mind if I get a picture of it?"

"I don't care," Trisha answered and moved her hair to one side to fully expose the tattoo on the side of her neck. Detective Barnes took a photo to later research if there was any gang affiliation.

"Are you hungry? How about we eat and talk some more?" Detective Korek asked and Trisha readily agreed to go to the nearby McDonald's.

"I'm going to call Carmella," Detective Korek said and Detective Barnes nodded.

After they ordered their food, they sat at a booth in the corner to allow for some privacy. Trisha immediately started eating her cheeseburger and fries, taking large bites without much chewing.

"Slow down there, we've got all afternoon to eat and talk."

"I've got to get back before Rico or Carlo returns," Trisha stated and suddenly comprehended that she was in public with two police detectives.

Detective Barnes quickly surmised it was the same men wanted in connection to the crimes in Louisville. He nodded to Korek.

"Honey, Rico and Carlo have a warrant out for their arrest. You aren't going back to the house, and he won't be able to hurt you again," Detective Korek told her.

"But what if you can't find them?" Trisha asked with concern. She shuddered at the thought of Rico being angry with her.

"We'll find them," Detective Barnes assured her. The Ft. Collins Police Department was watching the house and would alert the detectives when Rico and Carlo returned.

"Let's talk about you. You seem hungry. When was the last time you ate?" Detective Korek asked, and Trisha slowed down her eating slightly but was still grabbing four or five French fries at a time.

"Yesterday, I guess," Trisha answered.

"What did you eat?"

"Some cereal."

"Is that all you ate?"

"Yeah, that's all they gave me," Trisha answered, seeing no need to lie to the officers. "If we want food, we have to ask permission to get it."

"Is that why you're eating so fast, because you're worried about someone taking it away?"

"Mm-hmph," she mumbled with her mouth full and nodded her head.

"No one is going to take your food away. What school do you go to?" Detective Korek asked.

"I don't go anymore," Trisha said and took a large gulp of her milkshake. The bounty of food kept her talkative.

"How come you're not in school?"

"I don't know," Trisha reluctantly answered.

"What grade are you in?"

"I guess I should be in seventh grade. Am I in trouble?" Trisha asked with some trepidation.

"Definitely not. We want to know more about you. If you're not in school, what do you do all day?"

"Not much I guess," Trisha answered, ashamed to fully disclose her life.

"Are you allowed to come and go freely? Like if you wanted to visit a friend?" Detective Barnes inquired.

"I don't have any friends," she answered, and the detectives could see the dejection in her eyes as she quietly continued, "We're told to stay in the bedroom. Sometimes they let us out into the television room to play video games," she offered.

"The way you were treated, that was wrong. I hope you can see that," Detective Barnes commented.

"Yeah, I guess. There was nothing I could do about it."

"We know, and we're going to help you," Detective Korek told her gently. Trisha smiled at her and responded to the kindness projected by the detectives. It was so rare for Trisha that it sparked her deep desire for real caring from an adult, someone like she dreamed her mom would be like.

"There's Carmella," Detective Korek stated and waved her arm to get her attention. She came over to the booth.

"I want to introduce you to Carmella Locascio. She is here to help you," the detective told Trisha. Carmella was a victim specialist and would lead the assessment on how best to help Trisha.

"Okay," Trisha responded.

"I'm so glad to meet you, and I'll make sure you get everything you need," Carmella told her.

"We want to ask you some questions about the guys in the house. Is that okay with you?" Detective Barnes asked.

"I suppose so."

"Who is Jay?"

"He's a friend of Rico and Carlo. But, he's only been coming around for a little while."

"Are either of them a relative? Or maybe a foster parent?" Detective Korek asked.

"No. I used to be with a foster family, but I ran away," Trisha replied and took another gulp of her milkshake.

"Who are they?"

"They're the ones in charge of us."

"Where are they now?" Detective Barnes asked.

"I don't know."

"How did you come to live with Rico and Carlo?"

"Carlo found me. In a McDonald's like this. He said he was going to help me find my mom, but he never did," Trisha said and looked down with obvious disappointment.

"And you all live together?"

"Yes, but *Rico's the boss*," she answered in a serious tone. Detective Barnes concluded that the pair were probably the same Rico and Carlo that have been on the run for the last six months, and he nodded at Detective Korek in understanding. But the more pressing issue was the location of the other kids.

"You mentioned there were other kids in the house? Do you remember their names?" the detective asked.

"Sure, it's Rudy, Maureen, and Cassie," Trisha answered.

Detective Barnes displayed a picture on his phone and showed it to Trisha. Her face immediately went ash white before he could ask if she recognized the girl.

"Cassie," Trisha replied solemnly.

"Is Cassie in the house too?" Detective Barnes inquired.

"Yes. Well, I mean, she was," Trisha answered and started crying and croaked, "It's all my fault!" Trisha looked down and wouldn't make eye contact. She pushed her remaining cheeseburger away from her.

"It's okay, honey," Carmella said and cautiously took Trish's hand in hers. "Where's Cassie now?"

"He stepped on the back of her neck and she died. But it's all my fault," she wailed and started crying uncontrollably.

They gave Trisha a moment and Detective Korek moved to the other side of the booth and embraced the girl.

"I know it's hard, but can you tell us what happened? Take your time, sweetie," Detective Korek coaxed. After a few seconds, Trisha nodded her head and explained.

"Cassie was trying to contact her aunt to get out of the life. I ratted on her so I could get some new clothes. I didn't think Rico was going to get *so* mad. I thought he'd just yell at her or make her do more of the gross stuff." She kept her head down and was afraid to look at the detectives.

"It's all right. We are here to help get out of this situation," Detective Korek stated.

"When you say, 'made to do gross stuff,' can you tell me more about that?" Detective Barnes asked.

"Yes," Trisha finally answered after a long pause and started crying again.

Detective Korek gently stroked her hair with one hand and held Trisha's other hand. Trisha continued, "He makes us do that stuff with strangers all the time. Otherwise, I'll get kicked out of the house."

"What kind of stuff do you mean?"

"Sex stuff," Trisha bluntly said and looked down, filled with shame. The detectives were momentarily silent.

"I think that's enough for now," Detective Barnes concluded.

"I agree, let's take a break from the questions," Carmella suggested while looking at Trisha.

"Okay," Trisha answered

"You'll never have to go back to that house," Detective Korek

HIDING IN PLAIN SIGHT

assured her and Trisha nodded her head and wiped a tear from her eye.

"I'm going to assemble a team to help you," Carmella told Trisha. "We're going to get you checked out by a doctor, and I'll make sure you get dinner and have a nice place to sleep tonight. How does that sound?"

"Fine, I guess," Trisha answered.

Over the next few days, Carmella would assist Trisha and set her up with temporary housing, medical care, a caseworker, and a guardian ad litem. The guardian is appointed by the court to act as an attorney on Trisha's behalf and look out for her best interest. After Trisha was settled, the detectives would talk to her to gather more evidence and video record the discussion. Carmella would join the interview to support Trisha during the delicate process.

This girl is only four years older than my daughter, Detective Barnes thought to himself. *How heart-wrenching what this girl has gone through. She needs to be protected.*

Detectives Barnes and Korek then received a text that Rico and Carlo returned to the house.

"I'll alert SWAT to be ready to go in once we know what we're dealing with." Detective Korek stated.

"Can I finish my lunch now?" Trisha asked.

"Yes. Trisha, I have something for you," Carmella said and handed her a small tote bag that included a toothbrush, toothpaste, dental floss, soap, shampoo, a hairbrush, and feminine hygiene products–plus three pairs of fresh underwear, shirts, pants, and socks.

"Wow, that's all for me?" Trisha asked with amazement.

"It is, but the clothes might not be your exact size. I know all of this might be confusing and scary. We are going to get you to a safe place, and there are a lot of people that want to help you, so let them."

4 DAYS LATER

"I heard it was a successful operation," Carmella stated.

"It sure was. SWAT arrested Rico and Carlo and no one got hurt. The other kids were there too," Detective Barnes answered.

"Maureen and Rudy have also been referred over to human services," commented Carmella. The two were chatting in the break room of the task force building.

"That's good. I talked to the prosecutor, and they're making a deal with Carlo and Jay to testify against Rico for everything, including Cassie's murder."

"That's great–he should go away for a long time."

"They were into more than human trafficking. We're investigating them on illegal guns, drugs, and counterfeiting. There is going to be a lot of evidence to sift through."

"Counterfeiting too?" commented a surprised Carmella.

"Jay was the mastermind behind the printing. He would create the counterfeit bills and buy gift cards, running over $150,000 of phony bills through several Target stores.

"And Rico was getting into that activity too?"

"Yes, Jay confessed how they printed up $25,000 in a hotel room last week, and Rico had thousands of dollars in gift cards hidden in the house."

"It sounds like you should have a strong case."

"We should, but I'm always worried about it," Detective Barnes admitted. "We're always concerned about making the most solid case possible, and if we have enough evidence."

"I understand. Plus, you never know what a jury is going to think."

"Most of the public don't know anything about underage kids being sex trafficked, so sometimes it's hard for juries to believe what's actually happening," Detective Barnes added.

"It is right here under our noses, hiding in plain sight in suburban America."

"Well, I know it's not going away because both our jobs are getting busier every week," replied the detective.

"It's such a unique and difficult job that we do. It's too bad that most of the public doesn't know much about it," Carmella quipped.

"Yes, we see the most disturbing types of crime. Even other police officers tell me that they wouldn't want my job," Detective Barnes cited.

"Same with my coworkers," Carmella agreed.

"Victims of sex trafficking don't last more than seven years, and I don't mean that's how long they're being trafficked. That's their life expectancy."

"Yeah, look at Cassie who was trafficked for over two years and then was murdered by her pimp. Most of the time, we see these people after they have been abused for years. It's a difficult road of recovery," Carmella volunteered.

"I've seen tragedy, too, when they overdose on drugs or commit suicide. And those are the cases we know about. There's too many that we don't know about," Detective Barnes concluded.

"There aren't many good endings in our line of work."

"But getting Rico and Carlo off the streets prevented a lot of destruction in those kids' lives. *That arrest felt good.* How is Trisha doing?"

"Better, but she is in a tough situation, and she is going to have a long road ahead," Carmella replied.

"I wish I could give her a big hug and make it all go away."

"The longer she is away from her situation, the better she'll be. The last time I talked to her, she wanted to thank both of us."

"That was sweet. She seems like a tough little kid," Detective Barnes observed.

"Unfortunately, it was worse for her because she's been in and out of the foster system for years and was previously sexually abused."

"I didn't know that. So many of the sex-trafficked victims have a history of being abused. It's hard to imagine everything that she's gone through, all at the tender age of thirteen. Sometimes, it's incomprehensible to think about it," Detective Barnes added.

"That was their life *every single day*."

"It's a shame that our society has become so oblivious. They don't see Trisha as someone's daughter or sister. The sex buyer viewed it like an impersonal transaction instead," Detective Barnes added.

"Yes, the demand side is difficult to curb. Their actions come at someone else's expense, and many of these buyers don't realize how it's so damaging to the victim and to themselves," Carmella stated with disgust.

"I agree, and our modern society is so sexualized. Many of the buyers are more brazen and willing to take risks."

"They are pushing the envelope on the boundaries of what is considered sexual norms," Carmella replied.

"Most of them are unhappy people," Detective Barnes surmised.

"I sense that, too. If you can't find meaning in your own life, you try to fill it with pleasure, which is short-term and never lasts."

"Amen," Detective Barnes agreed.

18 MONTHS LATER, APRIL 2021

Rico was convicted of multiple crimes, including murder and sex trafficking of a minor, and received a three-hundred-and-eight-year prison term.

Carlo testified against Rico and pled guilty to multiple crimes, including sex trafficking of a minor, and received a fifty-four-year prison term.

Jay testified against Rico and pled guilty to counterfeiting and received a nine-year prison term.

Trisha was placed with a new foster family that lovingly took care of her. She's back in school and continues to attend counseling. She struggles to live every day as a survivor of her childhood nightmare.

3
I LOOK LIKE YOU

ANGELA RAE CLARK

GRAND JUNCTION, CO, JANUARY 27, 2018

* * *

When the sharpest words wanna cut me down
I'm gonna send a flood, gonna drown them out
I am brave, I am bruised
I am who I'm meant to be, this is me
Look out 'cause here I come
And I'm marching on to the beat I drum
I'm not scared to be seen
I make no apologies, this is me

> *"This is Me" – Keala Settle, from the motion*
> *picture,* The Greatest Showman

PART 1

There was a moment of silence as the crowd collectively decided the appropriate reaction. Everyone inhaled a deep breath, including Angela. The spotlights shone bright, focusing their attention on the woman standing alone on the stage. She could see their faces still processing the details of her story.

Angela briefly smiled and slightly nodded her head, indicating the nonverbal cue to the audience that her talk was finished. As if prompted, they erupted with applause. Two women stood up, and it instantly encouraged the entire audience to get on their feet to show appreciation for what they'd witnessed.

Angela Rae Clark soaked it all in. The bright lights, the auditorium crowd, the clapping, and the look on over 200 faces. Their expressions were emotional, not with pity, but instead with engrossed appreciation.

They respected her courage, perseverance, and the healing process she obviously had to go through that enabled her enough to share her history. The crowd responded to the most compelling story of the evening. As her audience stood and applauded her, they were awestruck that someone could have endured what she had experienced and have the emotional means to share it on a stage with strangers. Angela, too, was mesmerized, for she never expected a standing ovation.

The daylong event included a variety of speakers, ranging on topics from living sustainably to adventure excursions with wounded vets. Angela spoke in the evening, and her story was a unique personal account. It struck deep in the heart of the audience, for they knew it was not easy to tell, let alone live.

Angela admitted her struggles and lifelong journey of pain. But that long difficult trek also included healing and forgiveness, which culminated with her TEDx talk on the western slope of Colorado.

Angela, herself, was an avid watcher of TED talks on YouTube. There was an endless series of topics to watch, and she learned much and was impressed with the expertise of many presenters. Almost on a whim, she applied to speak at this evening's presentation and was nervous about living up to the expectations of TED speakers. They were always so interesting, educational, and informative. Angela felt inspired and hopeful when she heard stories of success and overcoming adversity.

She marveled that she was now one of those speakers. Little ole Angela Rae Clark from nowhere Iowa was on stage telling *her story*, earning a standing ovation no less, the only one of the event. She revealed the horrors of her childhood and the decades-long recovery process to live as a survivor. She didn't use notes or a PowerPoint presentation, but none was needed. Speaking from the heart and reading her poems and letters, she connected with the crowd in a more powerful way than any visual could provide.

Angela's breathing became erratic as emotion filled her body, mind, and spirit. The crowd continued the ovation, and she saw this moment as a culmination of her catalog of life experiences.

Yes, she endured moments of agony, but this evening wouldn't have happened without her willful determination. She was the sum of the failures and triumphs, all her battles with demons both inside and out. There were moments when it seemed like all was lost and there was no way out of the darkness. But her life was a testament to the daily fight to keep the darkness in check.

Angela remained on stage for an extra moment, placed her hand on her heart, lowered her head for a bow, and thanked the audience. She slowly walked off the stage, light on her feet with peace in her heart.

Strength and confidence raised the level of endorphins pulsing inside her brain. Angela wasn't given a map or a compass, but instead persisted along the bumpy and broken road to arrive in

Grand Junction. She recognized that public speaking and telling her story would play a significant role in her future.

16,835 DAYS EARLIER
CHRISTMAS DAY, 1971,
RURAL IOWA, AGE 3

The bottle advertised *genuine Kentucky whiskey*, but it wasn't the Bluegrass State's finest. It was harsh and seared his throat like turpentine. Cheap whiskey will do that every time, but he didn't care, for he was used to it; in fact, he embraced the burn.

It was only 9:30 a.m., too early for most people to start drinking, but not Clarence. He was already on the sauce, without regard to what day it was. It didn't matter. What mattered was that he woke up in the old farmhouse in an ornery mood.

He hoped that having a bright and cheerful grandchild would alleviate his pain, but it didn't. It only made him feel worse, seeing her happiness and innocence with her whole life ahead of her. What did she know of everything he'd been through? *Nothing.*

He escaped home by joining the army and vowed to never be on the losing end again. His granddaughter had no appreciation nor understanding of his trials overseas, fighting the Japs three decades earlier. Time had not healed his wounds.

She had no idea what it was like for him, seeing his friends blown to bits, dying in front of him, or worse, maimed for life. No one understood his physical frustration of marrying only a few weeks before boot camp. He shook the war memory out of his head, but it didn't help.

His thoughts drifted further back in his past, to his childhood and more painful memories of being beaten with a leather strap. It didn't make a difference if he deserved it or not. He received regular whippings and no one batted an eye. Such was life growing up in the Depression. Sometimes as punishment, he was locked in the barn on bone-chilling Iowa winter evenings. But if truth be told, it wasn't the beatings that really tormented his memories.

He was made to do things, disgusting things that he didn't understand as a child. He also witnessed what was done to his sister. *Keep it quiet,* he was always told, *don't air the dirty laundry. Keep it in the family,* he was threatened. Well, he never forgot and never told.

Clarence brought Angela into the laundry room and sat her on top of the washer. He looked at her and saw happiness, but it wasn't enough to soften his heart. Childhood wonder and simple joy would never be enough to alleviate his pain.

He couldn't see Angela's innocence or her potential, for he merely saw his own failures. Alcohol was rarely enough to dull the hurt and never enough to provide lasting soulful comfort. He was told repeatedly that he wouldn't amount to anything. He proved them right. Who cared about his pain? Who cared about making him feel better? Who cared about his heavy burdens? Who cared that his childhood was a disaster? *No one!*

He was disappointed that he couldn't find solace. No, it was more than disappointment, he was angry that Angela couldn't fix his sadness nor take away his loneliness. In his mind, it was her failure, not his.

She betrayed his hope for consolation, and *she* needed to be taught a lesson about how hard life could be on a poor man's farm. It was irrelevant that no three-year-old in the world could soothe his tortured and selfish soul.

He alone had the power to teach her a lesson, and nothing was going to stop him from flexing his authority. He'd done it before to others, and he would surely do it again. Hiding behind the washing machine was an electronic cattle prod.

He lifted it up and paused a moment to look and listen to see if anyone was coming. That would merely delay his actions. Angela reached out her hand with curiosity. Her inquisitiveness instantly stopped when he slowly placed the prod on top of her thigh.

She instantly jumped in shock from the unexpected pain and immediately looked at her grandfather. Her face cringed from surprise and the sharp agony that was forced upon her. She started crying and her grandfather put his finger to his lips to try and shush the child, but she kept on wailing.

He touched her again with the prod and inflicted more hurt so that Angela's tiny leg muscle twitched from the electrical pulse. Clarence sat in silence and watched his granddaughter react to his torture. It was his turn to do the inflicting. Once again, the family legacy was brought to *a new generation.*

"Hush now; this is our secret, ya hear? If you say anything to anyone, you'll get more," he menacingly told her. Angela could only cry and shake her head, wanting no more of the mean stick her grandfather held.

He had complete control over her fate and inwardly smiled from the domination he possessed over this toddler. It was comfort from the devil. The child had no other choice but to bend to his will, and this aroused him. So, he did it again and shot her with piercing electricity for a third time, and this time she howled uncontrollably.

Angela shrieked from the confusion and excruciating pain that her three-year-old brain could not process. *Why was Grandpa hurting me?*

Clarence knew that the child caused enough noise to get his wife's attention. He placed her on the ground and she immediately sat down. He lifted her up and coaxed her to walk forward towards the kitchen. He called for his wife.

Angela walked into the kitchen a few steps and then sat down on the floor and continued to cry. Cheryl entered within a few seconds and Angela, desiring comfort, put out her arms, and her grandmother immediately picked her up.

"She tripped," Clarence said without emotion and then added, "I think she may have scraped her knee," he lied. Cheryl looked at him with suspicious scorn but remained silent and inspected Angela's leg, which was dark red with swollen burn marks, but didn't look scraped as you'd expect from falling. A Band-Aid wasn't going to help.

Her grandmother tried to soothe her, but it wasn't working. She glared back at Clarence and took her to the bathroom to see if a warm bath would help. It wouldn't; the pain in her leg simply was too strong, and Angela continued to cry.

* * *

The only thing necessary for the triumph of evil is for good men to do nothing.

- *Typically credited to Edmund Burke*
(although researchers disagree as to its origin)

LATE AUGUST 1973, AGE 5

The Polaroid Land Model 95A was first released in 1948 and was dubbed the "picture-in-a-minute" camera, because the film developed quickly, right before the photographer's eyes. They hired a talented photographer as a technical consultant. His name was Ansel Adams. It would be another fifteen years before Polaroid would sell color film, and it would take until 1972 before the instant camera would be more economically available to the average citizen.

The Polaroid 100 was breakthrough technology, the Apple Computer of its day. It retailed for a hefty cost of $165. But to some, it was worth every penny. Physicist and inventor Dr. Edwin Land never imagined that the fruits of his inspiration would be used for insidious purposes.

"Check this out!" Clarence whooped, slapped the small Polaroid picture against his leg, and reached out to show the guys an image of Angela standing in a bathtub.

Earl immediately grabbed it and whistled. After staring at the picture for a long ten seconds, he commented, "This will be a great addition to my scrapbook!"

Clarence nodded and took another swig from the bottle. It burned his throat as usual but he let out an approving, "Ahhh." He flashed a wicked smile at his granddaughter and the little girl Earl brought.

"Let me see that," Chuck demanded and grabbed the picture out of Earl's hand. He too stared at it.

"That will cost you a dollar. Film is expensive, you know," Clarence bemoaned. "Unless you have a picture to trade."

"I got one for the collection too," Benny chimed in and pulled a picture out of his pocket to show the other men.

Clarence nodded with approval. The Polaroid camera and film were pricey, but since the picture would develop instantly, there was no need to get a roll of film to be processed. Their gratification was also instant and avoided the risk of their pictures being noticed at a photo lab. Clarence considered it the greatest invention of his day, and he cheerfully drove to Des Moines a few months ago to purchase the camera. It was worth it to get his friends riled up and always have a new Polaroid picture to sell.

He enjoyed being the hero of his small club. He took his pack of Winston cigarettes out of his denim shirt pocket and lit a match.

He deeply inhaled the smoke and then said, "Don't fight over the pictures. I have more film."

"Well, let's get on with it," Chuck encouraged and put his hand outward towards Clarence, indicating his desire for a swig of whiskey.

"Here you go, pass it around," Clarence laughed heartily and handed over the bottle, the alcohol fueling his temporary happiness. When he came down from the alcohol high, his happiness would transform into depression.

Clarence met his friends twelve miles from the family farm at Chuck's barn. Chuck lived alone and worked in town at the factory. He didn't own a farm or many acres, but like everyone in Iowa, his property included a barn. The other men, Earl and Benny, were local farmers like Clarence.

They'd been meeting in this barn for over a decade to enjoy their perverted pleasures. Originally, it started out looking at girlie magazines, but that was unsatisfying. The females in the magazine were too womanly, too shapely, and too developed.

Succinctly explained, they looked too much like what they were, *women.* They were acceptable as an appetizer, but these men wanted to feast. They now met at the barn for something much more sinister: They were renting out children.

With the popularity of instant photography in the early 1970s, the men started a collection of nude pictures. The color images excited the dark areas of their mind and the pictures of the children allowed them to relive their experiences over and over. It became an addiction and each man carefully hid a scrapbook. It was simply too easy and they obsessively added new material to their child pornography collection.

Holding Clarence's left hand was five-year-old Angela. This was her initiation. She wasn't the first brought there by Clarence, nor would she be the last. Clarence noticed Chuck staring at her.

"Well, if you want her, it's going to cost you forty-five dollars!" Clarence exclaimed.

"Forty-five dollars? What are you talking about? That's way too much!" Chuck balked.

"Well, it costs more since it's the first time I brought her. You get to break her in!" Clarence advertised and again heartily laughed. He knew of Chuck's willingness to pay to be the *first,* and he purposely started the price too high. It was all part of the game.

"Don't give me any of that crap. There's no way you would let any of us be her *actual first.* I know you've had her dozens of times!" Chuck countered, for he knew Clarence's habits and impulses well. Earl and Benny joined in with laughter, the grim shadows in the barn dancing across their faces.

Clarence stood silent and grinned from ear to ear, confirming to Earl and Benny that he'd already sexually abused Angela many times. The loud alcohol-infused laughter scared Angela, who tried to hide behind her grandfather's leg. Also in the barn was Earl's six-year-old neighbor, who similarly cowered from fright.

Clarence didn't want to exchange her for the other girl. There would be time for that another day. He needed some fast cash so he was going to sell her to Chuck or Benny, who didn't bring anyone for the exchange.

Chuck fished into his pocket and said, "I can't afford forty-five dollars, you know that. I brought everything I have. Will twenty-five dollars work?"

"What about you, Benny? How much money did you bring to this little party we're having, hmmm?" Clarence asked in a way a used car salesman would talk, hoping to bid up the price.

"No, I only have twenty dollars, and I've been looking forward to having little Jane again," he answered, referring to Earl's neighbor girl.

Clarence tried to act genuinely annoyed and insulted at such a low offer for Angela, but he couldn't pull off the performance and slapped his thigh with laughter. He enjoyed being the center of attention and the life of the party.

"Okay Chuck, because we're such good friends, she's all yours. But you need to have her back by three p.m.," Clarence told him and snatched the twenty-five dollars from his hand before he could argue.

"Only a couple of hours?" Chuck protested.

"I have a bunch of errands to do and some supplies to pick up in town. I'll drop them off at home and meet you back here."

"I don't know. I was hoping to have her all day," Chuck countered.

"You know I'm her babysitter on Saturdays while my daughter and wife work on cutting hair at the beauty parlor. They work until four o'clock, so I need you done by three o'clock."

"I suppose," Chuck reluctantly agreed and shuffled his feet.

"Besides, you don't really need more time than that. You've got four hours," Clarence pointed out and then added, "Less time if you keep yapping."

"Fine, come back here at three," Chuck answered. He was anxious to get started. Angela was scared and started crying. She didn't know exactly what Chuck was going to do, but she figured it would be bad. She attempted to run away, but Clarence held onto her hand tightly and wouldn't let her go.

She instinctively knew she was in danger but was too young to fully comprehend what was about to happen with a strange man.

Clarence picked her up in his arms and handed her directly over to Chuck. Chuck delightfully cradled her, purposefully holding her bottom. Angela struggled, but Chuck then wielded his other hand to force her body into his, with her head just below Chuck's neck. He turned and started walking away from the others, oblivious to whatever they were doing. He heard them murmuring but tuned them out. His sole focus was on Angela.

He entered his house raring to go. She was tiring out from her futile attempt to escape. She peered at the unfamiliar surroundings of his house. Chuck locked the door behind him and drew in a deep breath of Angela's hair. It hadn't been washed in a few days, but to Chuck, it was perfect. It smelled like *youthful innocence.* That was the only hair that he could see on her body, which met with his approval.

Chuck admired her aura of innocence, and he intended to explore every inch of it and release her from it. Her skin was soft with a fragile gentleness and untainted purity that made her appear like a little angel. She was *his angel* for the next four hours.

Her unsophisticated little body was warm and her unknowing eyes looked up at Chuck for answers and consolation. But his eyes only contained lust, for this was his fantasy come true. *She existed for his pleasure.* What was there not to love? And he was the lucky man who would shower her with lots of *love and affection* this afternoon.

He yearned to be alone with her and possessed the sole ability to choose what would happen and when. Every decision was his, and he was bursting with anticipation. He reached the top of the stairs, walked into his bedroom, and slowly shut the door.

EARLY OCTOBER 1977, AGE 9

"Hi sweetie, do you want some cereal?" Julie asked.

"I guess," Angela answered. Her mother stepped to the cupboard to retrieve the Frosted Flakes and noticed her yawn and rub her head.

"Are you feeling all right this morning?"

She let out a deep breath and answered, "Mom, my head hurts." Over the past several years, the headaches were getting worse and more frequent for little Angela.

"Maybe if you have a good breakfast, you'll feel better. How about I buy Cocoa Puffs the next time I'm at the store? You always like it when it makes chocolate milk, right?"

"Sure," she quietly replied, closed her eyes, and rubbed her temple a moment. Her mother placed the bowl of cereal on the table and poured some milk into it.

Her eyes brightened a little and said, "Did I tell you that I got an 'A' on my report about endangered animals?"

"You did?" Julie asked, and her daughter nodded her head. "That's wonderful. You're such a smart girl."

"I like school," she answered and thought back to the praise she received yesterday from her fourth-grade teacher, Ms. Emory, when she returned her two-page report. Angela was so happy when she saw her grade, with a little smiley face written by her teacher.

She thrived on receiving positive feedback from her teacher and was at the top of her class. She especially liked reading and writing.

Julie also enjoyed hearing about her daughter's academic success, living vicariously through Angela's student life. She knew Angela was safe at school, and it was the one place where she could still be a kid. But that knowledge was inadequate to provide joy to Julie's life.

There weren't enough "As" that her daughter could earn that would bring sunshine to cast away the shadows in Julie's life. Her daughter was trapped in the household and it was impossible for Angela to be the warrior angel her mother needed to save her from her own demons. Julie kept busy with work and volunteering at the church.

Perhaps if she didn't keep a demanding schedule, she wouldn't have been so conveniently distracted and unable to tune in to what was happening in her daughter's life. But maybe the long to-do list allowed her to pretend that everything was all right.

Angela sometimes wished her dad were around to hear about her good grades. Her parents divorced when she was two years old, soon after her brother was born. They moved in with her maternal grandparents, never seeing their birth dad who suffered from depression and frequently abused alcohol.

When she was eight years old, her mom remarried, and they moved to a nearby home, but that didn't stop her frequent interactions with her grandfather. Her stepfather legally adopted Angela and her brother. Unfortunately, her adoptive dad was riddled with anger issues and physically abused her, piling on the abuse.

"You've always earned good marks in English; maybe someday you'll be a writer," Julie suggested.

"I'd like that. Maybe I can write about my dreams."

"What did you dream about?" Julie asked with genuine interest.

"There are two that I remember. The first was when I was on a stage telling my story."

"Do you mean a stage like at the school play?"

"Sort of," she replied slowly with hesitation, collected her thoughts and continued, "It was just me on stage, you know, like the evangelists who come to our church. In the other dream, I was sitting in a room with another woman who was crying, and I was trying to help her." Angela started to get visibly tense.

"Why was she crying?" Julie casually asked.

"Because she was raped. I sometimes have nightmares of being raped," Angela bluntly stated and started crying and was about to continue before being interrupted by her mother.

"Where did you learn that word? That's not a nice word and you shouldn't say it to me or anyone else!" Julie exclaimed, bothered that her daughter spoke of such things.

"What do you mean, Mom? It was just dream," Angela answered with confusion.

"That may be so, but it isn't something you should be thinking about. Like I said, that's not a nice word."

"But . . ."

"But nothing," Julie condemned loudly. "You need to finish your cereal because I have to leave for work. Mrs. McKibbon is my first appointment, and you know how difficult she can be, so I gotta go."

"Yeah, okay," a dejected Angela replied and took another spoonful of her cereal.

"Hurry up, and then you go watch your favorite Saturday morning cartoon until Grandpa comes to watch you."

LATER THAT DAY

Angela arrived with her grandfather at Chuck's barn for this special occasion. No one else from Clarence's *club* was going to meet them in the barn today because this was to be a private transaction. Clarence jumped at the opportunity to sell Angela to a rich businessman.

Clarence made sure that Angela wore a thin blouse and shorts and left her sweater in his truck. He didn't care if she was cold on this brisk autumn Iowa morning. It wasn't every day that an out-of-towner was going to pay top dollar to have his way with Angela.

Clarence lit a cigarette and waited. Twenty-five minutes later he heard a car approach. He saw a Lincoln Continental abruptly stop, creating a cloud of dust in the dirt driveway. The *man in the suit* had arrived.

A fancy Lincoln was going to get noticed around town so they arranged for Chuck to be out of his house, allowing ample time and space for the man in the suit. Of course, Chuck would be paid for allowing his house to be utilized, and it was safer than having the man bring a little girl back to his hotel room, located in town near the factory.

"I'm Clarence, and this here is Angela," he said, and she looked at the man with great suspicion. The man did not introduce himself and immediately looked carefully over her for several moments, then frowned and asked, "How old is she?"

"Nine," her grandfather answered.

"She looks older than that, more like twelve or thirteen," he scoffed with disapproval.

Clarence was not about to lose the transaction, so he quickly remarked, "Sir, I can assure you that she's only nine years old."

"Then why is she getting bumps on top?" the man asked with annoyance. Angela was starting to show signs of feminine maturity. Clarence knew that it wouldn't be long before she'd age out and would no longer be desirable to her grandfather's *club*.

"She's just early I guess," Clarence explained.

Angela understood that they were talking about her, and that the man was unhappy with her. But she couldn't comprehend what she'd done wrong. Nine your old Angela once again wondered, *What's wrong with me?*

"Well, I don't like it, and she's not worth fifty dollars."

"You can hardly tell," Clarence countered and added, "I'll tell you what, why don't we settle on thirty-five dollars? You're here now and you have the entire house to yourself."

The man in the suit stroked his chin for a moment in thought and then answered, "Fine."

Angela was exchanged many times and knew what was about to happen. This was her sad expectation of what was normal.

Although the man was dressed nicely, it frightened her even more that she was being sold to someone who looked sophisticated and important.

"No!" she screamed in fright while hating the fact that she was born a girl.

"Shut up," her grandfather chastised her and pinched her arm to inflict pain and compliance. She continued to struggle and he looked at her directly and said, "You don't want me to get out the cattle prod, do you?" he asked with coldness and gravity.

Angela panicked and her stomach tightened. Her breathing was erratic and her face became flushed, knotted up physically with dread. The man in the suit grabbed her arm in a swift motion, and she reacted by using her other arm to hit him in the stomach. But her nine-year-old body was not strong enough to cause any damage nor deter the man. In fact, it egged him on.

"Oh, she's a feisty one!" he gleefully remarked.

"No, let me go," she cried in desperation.

"I'll get the cattle prod. That'll keep her in line," Clarence suggested but stopped talking when the man raised his hand for him to be quiet.

"No. I like it when they fight," the man in the suit commented with a devious smile and held his gaze on the child.

A few seconds later, he added, "We're going to get along just fine . . . just fine," he repeated. Squeezing her arm tighter, he again looked down to Angela, this time, his smile forever gone. *This child is mine.*

* * *

As Angela became a teenager, she physically developed as a young woman. No longer a child, this rapidly declined the interest of her grandfather and his friends. They moved on to a new set of victims. Angela could not remember the final time she was raped, and eventually, the exploitation faded away. But that didn't mean that she could return to a normal life, for her path was irrevocably altered.

As time went on and her childhood horrors became farther in the past, Angela subconsciously pushed the memories to the back recesses of her mind until they no longer were recalled. The abuse buried her memories deep in her subconscious. Her brain protected her with a common response called *trauma amnesia*. But make no mistake, those memories were there and found other ways to manifest and negatively affect her life.

As a teenager, Angela was tormented emotionally, which included depression, nightmares, suicidal thoughts, and difficulties working through stress. She also suffered physically, with frequent and severe migraine headaches, leg pain, and an uncontrollable twitching in her thigh.

Although she continued to perform well in school, some of her zeal and passion for academic studies had faded, especially in the subjects that held less interest to her. There still was one bright spot: she sustained excellent grades in English and loved to write.

Her adoptive father had a short temper and angered easily and would physically harm Angela. But her younger brother was treated harsher. He occasionally left bruises on both. She didn't talk to her friends about her physical abuse and no authorities were ever contacted.

1982, AGE 14

There is only one way to end the pain, she thought to herself. *I hate who I am, and my head is throbbing.* Angela's heart was racing, and she experienced palatable chest pain as she held the piece of broken glass in her hand. *My heart hurts so bad and there is only one way to escape.*

She stared at her arm and made a quick slice across her wrist and winced from the pain. It was deep enough to immediately start bleeding. Then she panicked that it was going to make a mess. She ran into the bathroom and wrapped it with a washcloth. The cut was surface level.

Her wrist hurt and throbbed with stinging pain. Fourteen-year-old Angela started crying from the combination of pain and dread. She held the cloth tightly around her wrist. *I hate my life*, she screamed inside her head.

She saw a bottle of Tylenol and shook it. It was half full. Pouring the entire contents of the bottle into her hand, she spilled some on the bathroom floor. Tossing several pills into her mouth, she grabbed a glass of water. She took the rest, including those that were on the floor.

Angela ran back into her bedroom and slammed the door. Still crying, she buried her face in her pillow. *Please, let me sleep forever*, she begged. She eventually stopped crying and fell asleep.

FOUR HOURS LATER

"Let's go!" her adoptive dad yelled up the stairs.

"Huh," Angela murmured to herself. She looked at the clock in her room and saw that she had slept all afternoon. She leapt out of bed, opened her bedroom door, and yelled down the stairs, "Okay."

"Make it snappy!"

"I'll be down in a minute," she answered and quickly put on clothes appropriate for the evening church services. She gazed at her wrist, which had stopped bleeding. Not bothering to clean her wound, she put on a dress with long sleeves so no one would notice.

PART 2, 1985, AGE 17

After graduating early from high school, she was encouraged to attend North Central Bible College near Minneapolis and major in sociology. Her mother expected her to utilize the college experience to find a husband. Angela viewed moving away to college as an escape from home. She hoped that removing herself from a toxic family would be a cure so she could lead a happy adult life.

If it were only that simple.

When she started college, Angela knew a young man from when she attended church youth camps. Within the first week, she started dating Darryl. Angela had a negative self-image, seeing herself as unattractive, uninteresting, and undesirable. She found it hard to believe that Darryl wanted to date her.

Darryl found Angela alluring, and after several months, they were engaged and she subsequently became an eighteen-year-old bride just before Christmas of 1986.

Angela hoped that this relationship would be the catalyst to keep her past in the past. She counted on her new husband to keep her safe and secure and help erase the hurt from her childhood. She disclosed to Darryl about her adoptive father's physical abuse and he observed her frequently sad and emotional moments.

Angela had conflicting feelings about body image, sex, and intimacy. She sometimes found it enjoyable, but it always felt dirty afterwards. She was struggling to find answers about the root cause of her views about sex with her husband.

Darryl loved her and wanted to help her through the tough times. He was patient and supported her through the ups and downs of their early marriage.

1990, AGE 22

Angela was living in Des Moines, Iowa, and pregnant with her first child. She continued to battle depression and had difficulties with the daily pressures of being married. She stopped her college coursework and recognized that her emotional challenges weren't getting better on her own, so in October, she sought help from a licensed therapist. Most of the therapists she worked with had acquired non-medical advanced degrees but weren't commonly referred to as a doctor.

"I'm sorry I'm late," exclaimed a frazzled Angela.

"Don't worry. And you can call me *Ma Freud* if that makes you feel more at ease," Lynn Mitchell told her.

"Ma Freud, that's pretty catchy," she replied and couldn't help but laugh. She caught herself chuckling and quickly clammed up, as if embarrassed.

She squirmed in the comfortable leather chair as she sat across from Lynn in the small plain office. She noticed some framed pictures containing small children and guessed that they were her grandchildren. Mrs. Mitchell was on her insurance plan, and she hoped that someone as old as her therapist, who was about fifty, could relate to her situation and help her cope with her problems.

"On the new patient form, it says you often feel anger, depression, and have a strained relationship with your mother," Lynn commented.

"That's right," she answered and squirmed in her chair again, trying to get her eight-month pregnant body comfortable.

"So, why seek help now?"

"I started with Doug Kuykendall back in April, but I recently ran out of sessions that the insurance would cover. He referred me to you since you are trying to build up your practice."

"Yes, I'm providing new patients with a large discount, so thanks for coming. But more importantly, did something recently happen for you to initiate therapy?"

"Sort of. I'm still dealing with problems from my childhood. Now that I'm going to be a mother in a couple of weeks, I want to address those issues," she answered and subconsciously rubbed her belly.

"That's good, tell me what happened."

"My adoptive father used to hurt us growing up. He beat my younger brother too; he always got it worse than me," Angela explained.

"He physically abused you?" Ma Freud asked for clarity.

"Yes, he would slap me and occasionally punch me. Sometimes, I would have bruises on my body. This went on for several years."

"And where does your mother fit into the picture?"

"My mother wouldn't do anything about it!" she condemned in a louder voice.

"When did the abuse start?"

"In elementary school, but it stopped by the end of high school."

"Were there any calls to the police or Children's Protective Services?"

"Nope," she answered, and her therapist wrinkled her nose slightly, indicating her disapproval of her mother handling the situation with willful blindness.

Ma Freud paused a moment and then asked, "What is your relationship like with your mother now?"

"We don't get along. I sure don't want to be a mother like her," Angela briskly stated, "That's why I'm here."

"That would be expected, these feelings of resentment."

"I don't want to be *anything* like her," she repeated with more emphasis and continued, "If my mother wants more salt on her food, I ask for pepper. I want to be the opposite of her. These feelings are more intense now that I'm going to have my own child."

"What about your marriage? How is your relationship with your husband?"

"He doesn't lay a hand on me, if that's what you're asking."

"Is he supportive of you seeing a therapist?"

"Yes, he's glad that I'm seeking help. I should have done it sooner. He's getting tired of me leaning on him emotionally."

"We'll talk more about your marriage at a future session, but before I forget, I want to ask about something you did when you first sat down."

"What's that?"

"When you first came in and I told you that my nickname was Ma Freud, you laughed but then immediately shut down. What were you thinking about in that moment?"

"You're right. I hate my laugh."

"Why is that?"

"I've been told growing up that I have my mother's laugh. So, I can't stand the way I sound. I didn't catch myself and usually try to laugh in a different way."

"I understand. Let me see if I have heard you accurately. There is a pattern of physical abuse when you were younger and your mother's lack of intervention for either yourself or your brother compounded your trauma. I believe you have feelings of resentment," Ma Freud summarized.

"Yes, we were both trapped."

"We'll explore that to look for the connection to your current emotional turmoil and depression."

"Do you think you can help me?" Angela asked.

"I think so, working together, I'm optimistic for you. Also, you have migraines frequently. This is common for people who've had childhood trauma."

"Is it?"

"Yes, you've suffered in the past, and it sounds like you've disassociated with your mother from a physical distance perspective, leaving home for college and getting married, but you also separated from her in an emotional and mental way," Ma Freud observed.

"Yes, I've been trying to get away from her."

"There are many unresolved issues that we're going to need to work through. The abuse is over, but obviously, it doesn't mean your pain is over."

* * *

Preparing for her next session, Ma Freud thought about everything that had yet to be discussed with Angela. She was keenly aware of her anger for her mother, but the therapist already discerned that there were deeper layers. Angela had difficulty remembering her early childhood, especially anything before the age of eight. Ma Freud speculated that there was more to the story. She was in the early stages of therapy with Angela, and she hoped that in time Angela would be able to approach deeper issues.

She wondered if *Angela's mother was abused as a child too?* Was it more than physical abuse? From Angela's perspective, her mother was an expert in denial and never wanted to talk about when Angela was in pain during her childhood. It left Angela angry and frustrated.

Ma Freud recently read a new book, *Secret Survivors* by E.S. Blume, which reviewed characteristics that can occur in the aftermath of incest. Thirty-four different behaviors were listed, and the more a person exhibited, the more likely the occurrence of incest. Ma Freud would be on the lookout during her appointments with Angela.

NOVEMBER 1990, AGE 22

One day before the birth of her first child, Angela's grandfather died of emphysema. But that didn't mean that her grandfather was out of her life.

Angela gave birth to her son, Bradley. The joy associated with having a new child was coupled with the difficulty of having someone so completely dependent. She was responsible for taking care of her baby's needs while also working to take care of herself. She continued to see Ma Freud on a regular basis to work through the negative emotions toward her mother and the physical abuse from her adoptive father.

New and more intense emotions were triggered by an event happening in Angela's daily life, such as the baby not sleeping well or getting sick. But she was unable to emotionally travel deeper to the root of her problems. She had a difficult time remembering large blocks of her childhood. Her therapy sessions focused on the resentment she harbored for her mother, whom she had no intention of forgiving. They also reviewed her emotions related to the birth of her first child and the death of her grandfather.

1991, AGE 23

Angela continued with Ma Freud and sometimes her insurance covered the sessions, but too often, the number of paid appointments ran out. She had limited funds but occasionally managed to find the money to pay her therapist. When money was tight, she was forced to discontinue her therapy. Sometimes, she attended group therapy, which was cheaper.

Changing jobs sometimes meant switching to a different insurance company, which inevitably mandated a new set of in-network providers. Frustration set in every time she started with someone new, for she had to start all over again.

She would also see a psychiatrist who had the authority to prescribe medicine. The only benefit of starting with a new doctor was that different ones preferred a different medication of choice. Angela was willing to try any new way to find relief.

It became a merry-go-round of prescriptions drugs, such as Prozac, Lithium, and Zoloft. Some worked slightly better than others, but none worked well enough for her to feel satisfied.

Some psychiatrists prescribed medication on the first visit. Angela noticed that medication was always the doctor's first choice of treatment. She was like most patients, desperately seeking to be on the *right* pill, so it would cure what was ailing her. Different doctors prescribed a variety of medications, and this went on for years with no real progress.

Different prescriptions caused a variety of side effects, including weight gain, sleepiness, nausea, dry eyes, and dry mouth. But the worst side effect was that it caused more frequent and intense *nightmares of being raped.*

She simultaneously worked with Ma Freud while also seeing a psychiatrist. As usual, unwelcome thoughts bombarded her peace, for Angela possessed an unquiet mind. To try to better understand what was manifesting itself through dreams and nightmares, Ma Freud suggested that Angela start a dream journal. She'd write about her nightmares and other thoughts, feelings, and experiences throughout the day.

* * *

In 1994, when Angela was twenty-six years old, she gave birth to a daughter, Frannie. This brought a new set of challenges, and she struggled daily to cope even with simple things like cooking a family dinner.

1996, AGE 28

Besides regularly seeing a therapist, she also saw a new psychiatrist, Dr. Renaldo Miller.

"Maybe I just need a different prescription," Angela asked with hopefulness. She didn't have childcare, so her daughter played on the floor in his simple office. Her son was in school.

"You've tried them all. We've carefully taken you through every family of medication and none have made a significant difference."

"What about something new on the market?" she asked.

"There isn't anything new to try, and I don't think it makes sense to continue changing your medication," Dr. Miller gently explained.

"Are you sure there isn't a better pill for me? I need something," she pleaded. "What else is there?"

"There isn't a pill to heal your broken heart. That's what you need to address, your broken heart."

Angela was initially confused. *What is a broken heart and how do I heal that?* She trusted Dr. Miller and considered him to be very practical. He'd helped Angela in ways that other doctors had not. For years, she was adamant that the right pill would be the final fix for her, but what he said made her curious about what to do next.

She wanted to be cured and done with seeing doctors and therapists. Over the years, she'd talked to other survivors of abuse and was jealous of those people farther along in the healing process. Jealous feelings bothered her, for she wanted to be the opposite of jealous, someone who was generous.

Dr. Miller noticed her frustration by her body language and continued speaking, "There isn't a quick fix. A *magic pill* doesn't exist."

"I know, I just wish . . ." she stated, knowing the reality of her healing journey. "What do you suggest I do?"

"Heal your broken heart." Because there was nothing else to prescribe, Angela was discharged from his care.

1997, AGE 29

"Mommy, you don't have to worry about making lunch today," little Bradley informed his mother. Angela was frantically running around the kitchen, trying to decide what lunch she would send him to school with. There weren't many choices because there wasn't much food in the house. This was because money was tight combined with not being on top of what groceries needed to be replenished. Angela had some difficulties managing the household.

"You need something for lunch," Angela insisted.

"We are going to get lunch when we visit the museum."

"What are you talking about?" she asked and then remembered that he was going on a class trip, and asked, "Is that today?"

"Yup, we're going to the dinosaur exhibit."

"Did I sign your class trip form?"

"No."

"I know that form is around here somewhere." Angela anxiously looked for the parental consent paperwork in the kitchen and various cabinet drawers.

Looking in the kitchen, she saw dishes piled up in the sink, and the "junk" drawer would barely open because it was stuffed with a variety of random objects. In the living room, laundry was piling up and the mess added to the confusion which made it harder to find the one-page piece of paper.

"Go look in your room; maybe it's in there."

"Okay," Bradley agreed while she continued to look throughout the small house. All she saw was chaos, which inflicted more stress and anguish.

She thought to herself, *Maybe Darryl took care of it?* But that was quickly dismissed as unlikely with Darryl working the night shift as a Sheriff's deputy. Her relationship with her husband was becoming more strained as the years rolled on, and he frequently lost his patience with Angela.

"Mom, why is the stove on?" Bradley asked, pointing to the gas range that was burning with nothing on it. She had every intention of making herself a cup of tea but forgot to put water in the kettle and heat it up. Angela ran over to the stovetop and turned off the flame. It was then she noticed Bradley holding a piece of paper.

"Is that it?"

"Yeah," he answered and handed the paper to his mother. She quickly read the form and filled it out. She was unhappy with the last line on the form: "*Include a check for $20 along with this form signed by a parent or guardian.*"

I don't know if I have twenty dollars, she thought to herself in a panic. Would her son be the only student left out? She dreaded the possibility of Bradley being singled out in an embarrassing way. He was looking up at her and then said, "I'm going to be late for the bus."

Angela continued to stress, but managed to push the negative thoughts out of her head and asked, "Where's my purse?"

Bradley silently pointed to a chair near the kitchen table. She went over to it, found her checkbook, and wrote a check for the field trip. She handed it to her son and hoped the check would clear.

Once the kids had left for school, Angela teared up and started crying. She thought to herself, *Why am I crying?* After all, her son was going to be able to make the field trip, so there was no reason to be upset. It didn't matter because her life was a hopelessly tangled mess. She couldn't stop herself for the rest of the morning and continuously cried *for the next four hours.*

PART 3, 1998, AGE 30

Angela and her children drove several hours through rural Iowa to visit family friends from the church she grew up in. As a child, she saw them frequently after mass and other social occasions. They were always kind to Angela, and even though she hadn't seen them in many years, she was looking forward to reconnecting with them. On the second evening of the visit, Nancy was preparing dinner in the kitchen. Angela was about to help her, but Sam asked her to sit on the couch. He wanted to talk.

"Your kids are playing in the other room, so this gives us a chance to talk," Sam told her.

Angela inwardly and outwardly cringed at the word *play*. That word reminded her of her grandfather. As an adult, she would never tell her kids to *go play*. She recoiled when an adult was joking around and suggested that she be *playful*. The word had serious negative connotations and brought her back to being a child and associating that word with something *icky*.

"I've been thinking about this ever since you planned your visit," Sam said deliberately. He noticed the disturbed expression on Angela's face but assumed that she guessed what he wanted to talk about or was reacting to his uncomfortableness.

"Okay," she slowly replied, unsure where the conversation was going.

"It's an awkward subject to bring up, but I feel it's long overdue," Sam started with that ominous statement and she instantly felt stress, her stomach tightened with nausea.

She didn't know what Sam was going to talk about, and she didn't want to have an awkward conversation. Angela was regularly going through difficult periods in her life, and she didn't come for a visit, only to argue with a family friend. She respected and got along well with Sam and Nancy and dreaded hearing his criticism. *Is that why Nancy left the room?*

She didn't want to be blamed for anything and was momentarily distracted, wracking her brain to figure out what she'd done wrong. She imagined the next session with her therapist would center around this new basis to feel miserable.

She couldn't think of a reason why Sam would be upset with her, especially since they hadn't seen each other in many years. But before her mind could go down any more ratholes, he started speaking, "I should've talked to you about this years ago."

Sam was about to continue before she interrupted him, "I'm sorry, Sam, for whatever I did," she implored.

Sam slightly shook his head in disagreement and said, "No, I want to thank you."

"Thank me?"

"Yes, for what you did as a teenager."

"What are you talking about," Angela stated, sincerely confused.

"This was when you were fifteen. Do you remember when our daughter Emily came to visit you for a few weeks during the summer?"

"Yes, I remember she had a nice visit, and since we're only a few years apart, it was like having a little sister to hang out with."

"Emily was shy back then; I guess she's still that way, not surprising considering everything she's been through," Sam explained.

"What do you mean?" Angela asked, for she hadn't seen Emily since that long-ago summer visit.

"I wanted to thank you for letting me know what was going on with Emily back then," he stated in a gentle way, his face flushed with embarrassment. She returned his gesture with her confusion.

"I was glad that I could help, but I don't remember having a conversation with you."

"I know it's awkward to talk about, but it was courageous of you to tell us about Emily's sexual abuse."

"Her abuse?" she asked with a gasp and stammered after hearing the unexpected reason for being thanked.

"Yes, I know that you were just a teenager too, but sometime during her visit, she confided in you that my brother-in-law was sexually abusing Emily, and it'd been going on for several years."

Angela was shocked and horrified to hear this from Sam, as if learning it for the first time. She instantly felt empathy for Emily and something stirred deep down inside her that caused her heart to skip a beat. She remembered something about Sam's sister and her husband getting divorced, but she hadn't thought about that in many years.

"You were unsure about telling me, but I'm so thankful that you did so I could stop what was happening. You knew it was wrong, and it put everything in motion," he explained. She stared at Sam with her mouth open, unable to formulate a response, so he continued.

"My sister and brother-in-law lived with us while they were getting settled with new jobs in town and unfortunately, he had access to Emily. Even after they moved out of our house, it continued at family functions and other times, right under my nose!" Sam stated with frustration and clenched his fist.

"I don't remember this at all," she admitted.

"I still blame myself for not realizing what was going on for many years," Sam cringed, trembling, reliving the moment.

"I am so sorry that happened to her."

"We talked to Emily, and she eventually told us what he did to her. We confronted my brother-in-law and the police were alerted. But it was worse than we thought."

"Worse?"

"Emily wasn't the only one he abused. Others came forward. It was so horrible. It still eats me up inside that he did those evil things to those kids," Sam stated, now highly agitated. He paused, took a deep breath, and added, "The important thing is that the abuse stopped."

Angela continued to process what Sam revealed, and she could feel her stomach acid churning from the stress. Picturing what Emily experienced, she physically felt ill the harder she thought about it.

"You look upset too; I'm sorry to bring this up," Sam apologized.

"Damn, I don't remember any of this. But if I helped interrupt Emily's abuse, then I'm pretty happy that I told you."

"I was very upset back then, but I don't know what would have happened to Emily if you didn't talk to me. I never thanked you for helping Emily, so that's why I brought it up today."

"I have no idea why I don't remember this."

2002, AGE 34

Angela worked in an office part-time and continued to struggle emotionally and physically, especially with migraine headaches, sometimes so severe that they incapacitated her, and she became dehydrated from vomiting. She barely worked enough hours to obtain medical coverage.

Migraines always prevented Angela from living a full life. The headaches impacted her marriage, her ability to work full-time, and the level of care she could provide to her children. In essence, it held her back from both her healing process and realizing her potential as a human being.

Angela helped a friend who needed a ride to an acupuncturist appointment. While her friend was being examined, she sat in the waiting room. She relaxed with the soothing music and pleasant aroma. The therapeutic environment calmed her. She read through their brochures and learned more about acupuncture and its benefits. The migraine she walked into the office with seemed to have melted away, so she decided to set up her own appointment.

After multiple sessions, her migraines lessened, and then one day, she realized that she forgot about managing her headaches because they were gone. It was much needed and allowed her to better concentrate on her work and life balance. Her acupuncturist suggested that she become active in managing and conquering small things to incrementally take control of her life. After years of battling migraines, the weight was lifted.

2003, AGE 35

Over the years, Angela kept a journal and the memories slowly continued to rise out of her subconscious. Unfortunately, her marriage to Darryl weakened and they drifted farther apart. She sought help from a marriage counselor, and Darryl attended a few meetings, but lost interest and stopped participating. He checked out of the marriage. He was no longer compassionate with her and became distant.

Darryl desperately wanted to make her happy in the early days, but in truth, no one can make someone else happy. At the age of thirty-five, the marriage ended after seventeen years, and she took care of their two children, ages nine and twelve.

* * *

It is time now, it is time now that we thrive
It is time we lead ourselves into the well
It is time now, and what a time to be alive
"We Shall be Known" – MaMuse

2005, AGE 37

Sitting in her therapist's office, Angela had to know if there was a monster inside of her. Was she forever tainted by her abuse? Was she abused so often that it turned her into a monster? She fought an internal battle, not with the monster itself, but with the doubt of her own goodness and the fear to confront it.

In addition to a therapist, she also sought help from Rachael, a healing arts practitioner. This involved utilizing a variety of techniques focused on physical, emotional, spiritual, and mental healing and recovery. Angela viewed the healing arts as an important part of a holistic approach for her. This sparked a thought for her, *Maybe someday I can be a healer too.*

After several sessions, she tentatively agreed to deeply explore her true self. But she didn't make any promises to her healer and energy coach.

"We've talked about this many times; the box that's in your heart. You previously indicated that you're willing to explore the possibility of opening the box," Rachael stated.

"Yes, but I'm scared," Angela answered, sighed loudly and closed her eyes for a moment, and then asked the question that was weighing her down, "What if I can't get rid of the monster inside the box?"

"Whatever is in there, we will deal with together. It's taken you years to get to this point, addressing your depression and anxiety. Your fear of what's inside the box has been a heavy burden."

"I know, because there's a monster in there! It's a super scary awful monster," she exclaimed.

"You've been fixated on that monster. It's impacted you as an adult in so many ways."

"Of course, because I know what's inside," she told her and then thought that this wasn't the right day to open the box.

Although Angela was certain there was a monster in her heart, there was also an unknown piece. *Just how terrible is it?* The monster isn't going anywhere, so maybe another day would be better?

"We need to address whatever is inside the box," Rachael encouraged. "If there's one thing I've learned about you over the past year, it's that you have determination. You want to understand and battle the demons inside. Including this one."

She knew Rachael was right. "Yes, all right, I'm ready," she agreed with reluctance.

"Let's see what's really there. I know you're scared, but I have confidence in your fortitude. You're the only one that can open the box. If there's a monster, I'm certain that you'll know exactly what to do."

"Trust me, there's a monster," Angela responded without hesitation.

"I'll be right beside you the entire way. We'll figure it out together and it will become clear."

"I've been talking about it with you for a long time, and I've been journaling about it too. I've wrestled with this, going back and forth, trying to decide if I dare look inside that box. But I'm already thirty-seven years old so I might as well deal with the monster."

"I'm here. Let's take that journey together. Are you ready?" Her eyes were already closed and she nodded her head. Rachael dimmed the lights in the office and lit a few scented candles that she knew Angela liked to help her relax.

Rachael guided her to regulate her breathing and allow her mind to be free. She invited her to a space of curiosity. Rachael helped empty her mind of stress, guilt, and worry. She imagined everything flowing outward. The negative thoughts were draining out of her consciousness. Then she allowed new thoughts to flow inward.

She imagined the large box in the distance, like a treasure chest with a lock on it. Angela was unsure of exactly what was inside but stepped closer. It was a long and lonely walk, but she finally made it. She imagined herself holding a key and putting her hand close to the lock. She put the key into the lock, turned it, and heard a *click*. It was unlocked. She removed it and clenched her fists, ready to fight back if necessary.

The lid to the box was still closed. There was still time to go back, still time to put the lock back on and run away. There was even time to douse the box with gasoline, light it on fire, and never find out what was inside.

She paused and then said, "I don't know if I can do it."

"You're doing great. If you want to turn back, it's okay. I won't push you. *You* have to want to open that box," Rachael softly reminded her. Perhaps it was in that moment when she was given the option to retreat that she found the courage to look inside the box. Now was the time.

She put both hands on top of it. It was heavy but she found the strength to lift it up. She slowly started pushing it higher and higher. She was expecting a creaking sound like you'd hear in a horror movie, but this box was silent. It was now completely open, but shadows darkened the inside.

She could tell there *was* something inside, but she couldn't see what it was or whether it was friend or foe. She would have to peer inside. Moving her body a little bit closer, she slowly bent down to look inside the darkness. *That's when its content was revealed.*

It was smaller than she expected. It didn't make a noise, and it looked directly at her. The creature inside was completely still. It was black and yellow and had large eyes that looked right through her.

It had short squat legs, but it didn't matter because this creature didn't need its legs. It used its *massive* wings. She recognized what the creature was. Her eyes opened wide with her mouth agape, reflexively reacting to the awestruck vision.

The creature slowly rose to give Angela a full view in the light. She couldn't have guessed what was in the box in a million years. The creature continued to rise, and she followed its every movement, no matter how subtle.

The creature was *free.* Soon, it floated so high that she could no longer see it. She marveled at the creature that came out of the box *in her heart.* A natural and relieved smile formed on Angela's face; she had witnessed the release of *her beautiful butterfly*, peacefully floating upwards, rising high in her view.

There wasn't a monster in the box, and her butterfly was free. And then a thousand more butterflies came out of the box.

2010, AGE 42

As part of her healing process, Angela started receiving spinal tuning sessions. These sessions were typically done in conjunction with chiropractic adjustments. The spinal tuning employed a whole mind-body connection by stimulating the sensory portion of the nervous system to relieve both physical and mental stress. After the sessions, she felt renewed and relaxed. The spinal tuning complemented the therapy and helped her benefit more from therapy.

She reviewed with Ma Freud the strained relationship as an adult she had with her grandfather, yet she wasn't certain of the root cause. Over the years, her mother would tell Angela that her grandfather loved his family very much, as if explaining away his bad behavior. She never could determine why her grandfather needed defending. Angela was frustrated that even after all these years since her grandfather passed, she still had questions about him and her mother's cover-up. But abuse like what Angela endured doesn't simply melt like the morning dew.

Angela then explained to Ma Freud about something that came to her in a dream. She told her about new memories of being shocked with a cattle prod on her thigh. She'd previously told Lynn about uncontrollable muscle twitching in her thigh that she'd been suffering for decades. Angela tried muscle relaxer medication, but it didn't stop it from happening.

"At what age do you think this memory is going back to?" Lynn asked.

"It's vague and a little foggy, but I think I was really young."

"Describe what you can remember," she encouraged.

"The oldest memory is when I was about three. But I also remember it happening later, when I was five or six. I see myself sitting in a classroom, and my thigh was twitching but I couldn't stop it. That was probably first or second grade. I don't think it was one time; I get the feeling it was happening on a regular basis."

"This is good; I think we're really getting somewhere."

"Yes, because this is a new memory from my childhood. I previously had no recollection of anything from such an early age."

"You talked about your adoptive father's abuse, but this memory is before he was in your life."

"Yes! I can see specific things, but it comes to me in small pieces," she explained.

"That's normal. Do you remember who was doing this to you?"

"No, I don't."

"Would you like to explore that memory with me?"

"I'll try," she replied and closed her eyes, steadied her breathing, and focused on slowly calming herself.

"Relax, take as much time as you need. Keep your eyes closed and just let your mind float back to that time, and see if this memory will be revealed," Ma Freud calmly instructed.

Angela allowed her mind to wander and drift. Fuzzy memories of sexual abuse were surfacing. She closed her eyelids tighter as she relived the pain from the cattle prod. She saw a long, toned, and tanned arm holding the cattle prod.

She could see herself as a little girl crying as soon as the electrical pulse shocked her thigh. Little Angela was too scared to look up to see who was perpetrating this against her. She didn't dare look and couldn't see a face, *but she heard a voice.*

The voice was berating her and threatening her to keep their *secret.* It was a thin raspy voice, the kind one usually gets after decades of smoking two packs a day. There was no denying that rough voice: *It was her grandfather.*

"That's enough for today. Let's bring you back into the room. We'll do a grounding exercise and bring you into the present time where you are safe."

* * *

ANGELA'S DREAM JOURNAL:
JANUARY 13, 2011

I have a dream of healthy, joyful and whole children that don't ever learn what the word *abuse* means. It's not in their vocabulary because it's not in their dictionary. How can this happen? By having healthy, joyful and whole people raising them and caring for them. At home, school, church, daycare and the homes of family and friends. What can I do? Just one person. Can I make a difference? My healing has to happen first, then I can share my story and help others to heal. It starts here, in my home, in my heart.

I have felt fractured all day. I can't connect the basic dots of where I need to be or where I need to go to be efficient about it. Normally, I am all about efficiency.

I feel like I have one thousand loose ends in my life that I would love to clip off and have a fresh slate. That is my goal. Can I get my life in order like that? Based on the last few months, the answer is no.

I had a hypnotherapy session today. In an effort to nurture myself, I also had an energy healing session and it was good. I did feel reluctant to go into the hypno-state, afraid of what I would find there. I think I totally chicken shitted the hour away. Where is my courage today?

I would love to have a good long hug tonight. I want to be held by someone that would let me draw on their strength and collect as many hugs as needed. I need some reassurance that I am going to be better than okay on the other end.

I feel hollow and empty. My friend "D" and I hung out for a bit. She clearly does not know what to do for me except medicate me. It was okay with me. We loaded up on some junk food and wine and mindless TV. I think I could be a junkie of any of the above if I allowed myself to go down that path.

The moon is beautiful, lending strength and courage to me. I see a child's face reflected in the moon tonight. I wish I could sleep outside with her.

PART 4, 2012, AGE 44

Angela continued living in Iowa and additional memories came out about how her grandfather physically tortured her. There wasn't any doubt. Once the source was identified in her mind, the pain in her leg and the thigh twitching stopped. She marveled that her years of suffering had miraculously disappeared. While that was good news, she was thrown a new challenge.

Memories of her sexual abuse surfaced, and she realized that it wasn't an isolated incident. She came to know that someone abused her sexually hundreds of times during her childhood. She also remembered being sold to neighbors at the barn as well as to complete strangers, such as *the man in the suit.*

Another family member disclosed an experience of abuse, with some members believing the person while others were in willful denial. This disclosure prompted more memories for Angela.

She remembered when she was twelve years old, playing with a younger cousin. Angela doesn't remember how the incident started but knows that she acted out with her cousin the same abuse that was inflicted on her.

She felt powerful and in control. In the moment, it wasn't about being sexual or erotic but for once, she was the one in charge. She wanted to rule over another and hold the fate of an innocent person, and don't forget the smugness of getting away with it.

Remembering her actions shocked and mortified her. As she thought more about it and allowed the full context of her memories to surface, she worried that her greatest fear might have been realized. *Was she a pedophile?* She thought about it for a long time, and over the years, only recalled doing that to someone else the one time.

Angela engaged in additional spinal tuning on her own and journaled about whatever came into her mind. But even if it occurred only once, she understood that it was one time too many. She looked harder and deeper at herself, more than ever before, concerned that she was full of malice, forever and irrevocably marred by the abuse.

She always saw her abuser as a faceless person, but after several more spinal tuning sessions, she slowly realized that her sexual abuse was inflicted by *her grandfather.* This resulted in grave stress and anxiety about who she really was.

She wondered if the events of her childhood permanently changed her into a bad person–an unworthy person and unlovable person. This anguish forced her to deeply self-reflect and wonder what was inside of her. *Was her heart destined to be forever broken?*

Or worse, was her heart forever darkened? Did the evil perpetuated on her become ingrained in her heart? Is it stuck and cannot be removed? Angela wondered, *What if I'm a bad person? What if I'm the evil one now?* She knew that this needed to be discussed with her therapist.

Angela felt intense trepidation about what she might find. How would she deal with the truth? What if she was horrified by what she saw?

She worked with a new licensed therapist, Susan Reinig. Susan explained, as others before her, that what had happened to Angela was not her fault. She was only a child when she was physically and sexually abused. Susan also clarified that the incident with her cousin was a result of her ongoing abuse.

"What did you say it's called?" Angela asked.

"The action falls under the category called *problematic child sexual behavior.* This is where a child, or adolescent in your case, acts out sexually against another child because of anger or anxiety. It is completely different than adults who sexually abuse children. The sexual behaviors of children are a direct reaction to their traumatic experience," Susan stated.

"I agree with what you are telling me, but I am still appalled and guilty about what I did."

"That's understandable. Specifically, in your case, it's described as *dual victimization.* Your actions were a learned behavior and even though you were the aggressor, you're both victims. Think of it like this: a schoolyard bully who acts out on a classmate is the direct result of he or she being abused at home."

"There is a cause and effect?"

"Yes. Let me reiterate, in no way did you deserve what happened to you. Even your actions at twelve are not your fault."

Intellectually, Angela understood this and agreed with the assessment. But emotionally, fear and doubt lingered in her mind, and she could not distance herself from the shame associated with her childhood. She felt dirty. She comprehended that part of the reason it took many years for memories to come out was that it was buried deep inside. Then Susan changed the subject, which made it a therapy session she'd never forget.

"There's something I've decided to share with you because it will be helpful to your process," Susan calmly announced.

"What's that?"

"I had a client a number of years ago who had similar experiences."

"Really?" she asked, and sat up slightly taller in the chair, her curiosity peaked.

"Yes. I believe that it's okay for me to tell you about this. It was about ten years ago, and unfortunately, he committed suicide."

"Oh, no," she answered with surprise and trepidation, for she was not expecting Susan's comments.

"He was from the same town you grew up in and had terrible memories of being raped in a barn by a group of men. It went on for years during his childhood."

Angela felt sick to her stomach and immediately imagined the horror that the boy endured. She was silent a moment and then asked, "Was it when I was a child?"

"Yes. It is very possible that you knew this person and were abused by the same people."

"Wow, I don't know what to say," she replied with a thousand different things racing through her head. Susan brought her back into focus.

"The reason I'm telling you this is because it *validates your memories. They're real,*" Susan stated with quiet authority. The importance was not lost on Angela.

"So, I am not crazy?" she blurted out.

"This points to the high likelihood that your memories are genuine," Susan explained, purposefully not repeating the word *crazy*.

"I've always wondered if my memories were real. In my gut, I thought it truly happened to me. But there was always lingering doubt. I'd rack my brain over and over, trying to figure out what was factual," she excitedly said, realizing the importance of the burden of doubt being lifted.

"This might calm down the part of your brain that is continually spinning cycles of doubt. This is independent evidence."

"I no longer need to question my sanity!" she beamed.

Susan smiled and then added, "You can let go of that worry and focus on healing."

"Yes, although I wish I could have helped him."

"Me too."

* * *

As Angela matured into her mid-forties, her children grew up and left the nest. She became better equipped to manage most aspects of her life and wished that she would've started the healing process earlier so she could've been a better mother to her children. She also joined and regularly participated in a few survivors' support groups. She bonded and felt a sisterhood with other women who suffered through a similar ordeal.

Perhaps it was time for her to take the next step. It was a baby step. She wasn't ready to forgive anyone, but for the first time, she saw that as a possibility. A few weeks later, Angela wrote in her journal:

"Planting Seeds: Someday I'd like to be FREE from the weight of UNFORGIVENESS. God, prepare my heart so when the moment arrives, I step into the miracle of unfolding."

2013, AGE 45

Angela continued to struggle with guilt and shame and was exhausted from using her energy to wish it away. Sitting alone in her kitchen, she continued to journal thoughts and emotions and wrote:

> I feel like I am drowning in shame. I take more of it in with each breath. It stinks like rotting flesh. Its voice is *eerily comforting* as it fills my ear with lies. Sometimes I play hide and seek with shame trying to escape its grip. But I end up feeling naked and exposed and put out the SOS - Shame Oh Shame, please return. Wrap yourself around me like a cloak and help me feel safe again.
>
> My head knows that being raped was never my fault, but I cannot release the grip of shame in my being. Okay, God, let's heal this shit. Enough already. I'm almost forty-six and I have proven I can do shame - with gusto, flair, and grit. *It is time to make a change.*

* * *

Angela experienced a memory recovery that involved her grandpa calling her feisty. She distinctly remembers that he clearly liked it when she fought back during the abuse. He would restrain Angela, who attempted to kick him. She wrote in her journal her thoughts and feelings:

Feisty for $25
25 dollars changes hands over my head
Dirty blue and white striped mattress
Iron headboard

Hot heavy air
Dirty sweaty man
Hands bound to iron
I twist, I turn
I kick
I FIGHT
With all I am I FIGHT
With a chuckle he says
"Just what I like, feisty"
My five-year-old brain scrambles
How can I NOT fight?
Fight or no fight, he wins
He unties me, tells me to run for the road
I fall, twist my ankle on broken dry dirt
Grandpa is there
He chuckles at my tears, my fear
He carries me to the car

* * *

The memory continued to reveal that he grinned and laughed in response to her struggling to fight back or escape. Angela thought further about how her grandfather called her feisty and wrote in her journal:

Feisty is a child struggling, fighting against something or someone bigger and not winning. An unproductive struggle. Going against bigger forces and not winning. A stubborn child refusing to cooperate.

Unproductive struggle summed up Angela's life. She often felt that her entire existence were a thousand struggles inside one giant one with no gain in sight. Decades of therapy left her frustrated and asking, *Why am I still in chaos?*

Then she looked up the word in several dictionaries, which revealed the layers of emotion that influenced her perception of the word.

> **Feisty:** *adjective*; having or showing strong determination, touchy, or aggressive. A second dictionary described the word as lively, determined, and courageous. A third, as full of spirit or determination; plucky or spunky.

After learning the true meaning of the word, she looked back at all the different ways she tried to interpret her memories. Angela's perception of the word was incorrect. Being *feisty* was better than she imagined.

Angela's life changed when she thought deeply about how it would feel if she no longer carried the weight of her trauma. This was a difficult concept because there was never a time *before* the trauma that she could compare it with.

Releasing the weight would come in only one way. She made the pivotal decision to forgive her grandfather. With her forgiveness, she was given the *gift of freedom*, which she heartily embraced. Angela wrote in her journal:

Dear Grandpa,

It's been years since the first memory emerged of you violating me in my tender years, revealing that my persistent nightmares of rape were rooted in truth. These memories have been fragile shadows always present in my life, waiting to be unearthed with care and respect.

In the earliest memories I did not know you, the perpetrator. The face on this male energy was a black cloud of pain, rage, and self-loathing that pulled compassion from me. As unbelievable as it seems, my compassion for you was spontaneously more palpable than for my Self; your pain was wildly vivid and accessible to me. My core Being felt the enormity of your angst, your struggle.

I think of this witnessing as a gift.

The impact of your self-loathing during my remembering brought me to my knees inside because I too, have loathed myself so completely that I was left gasping for breath and fighting with life. I finally understood the errant seed that had taken root so long ago.

After a few weeks, your face, your smell, your voice emerged from that black cloud. I had two grandpas. One that was in the photos of my recorded milestones and the other that was this monster and master of violence.

Soon, I found anger for you and your choices. I yelled until I lacked voice once again and punched the boxing bag wishing it was you, except then you wouldn't be dead. You did make things easier by exiting before you harmed another generation. I think it was the only way you knew how to stop. My son, your first great grandchild, was due any day so you exercised a rare bit of courage, and you died.

It seems a strange package, but anger for you delivered me to compassion for my Self. Finally, my unexpressed childhood was exposed. Grief and sorrow were first in line for all the years of black depression, migraines, anxieties, and unfounded fears that left me feeling gutted of the ability to experience basic pleasure in the micro or the macro of living.

It seems ridiculously backwards: compassion for you before my Self. However, I have accepted that healing unfolds in mysterious and miraculous ways.

Grandpa, I know you hated who you were. I don't believe in hell as an afterlife. I believe in healing. And healing in hell would be next to impossible.

I keep searching for healing, Grandpa, seeking more freedom. What if you had chosen to feel the world through my heart? What if you had stepped into my skin, and felt the vast cavern of fear and silence that held no markings for the path to healing and voice? Perhaps you would have found the strength to put a stop to this cycle of violence. Maybe you would have found compassion for your wounded Self in that space of Me.

Because compassion was my deliverer, I see a Circle of Compassion that holds every living being. I believe if we intentionally move through the circle, we will be richer and deeper as individuals, naturally stronger and more connected as a community.

It means we find our place on this circle and diligently move forward until we experience the weak, the sick, the young, the old, the strong, the healthy, the rich, the poor, the neglected, the abusers, the victims, the rapists, the advocates, the care givers, the judges and the animals, the Earth –leaving no living being untouched.

What if by visiting the depths of all that we have in common with each other we heal our deeply held wounds?

Living with compassion does not mean a life free of pain, but rather a life where communication, reconciliation, restoration, and healing are honorable, sought-after experiences.

What if we begin to imagine a world that does not understand the words violence, abuse, rape, neglect, and discrimination?

Somehow, I know you are listening, Grandpa.

–Angie, The Feisty One

THE NEXT WEEK

Angela underwent a breakthrough during a quiet moment one evening and wrote about her experience in her journal:

A little miracle occurred. I heard my grandpa saying "Angie" in quiet moments. Just before bed I said, "Okay, grandpa, I am listening." He appeared in my mind's eye sobbing and repeating, "I'm sorry."

I thanked him for his apology and released him to continue his own journey. While it was completely unexpected to hear from him because he died decades ago, it was beautiful to feel his sincerity and hear his apology. I certainly was not anticipating this experience.

So, if his soul found a new level of peace, that was previously beyond imagination, I am a-okay with that.

Won't you plant some heart seeds today?

The second miracle is that the SHAME that clouded my whole life, simply evaporated. I had not understood the roots of my shame until now. I had worked on it from so many angles, and now with the choice of forgiveness, it was gone.

I don't know if I can adequately express how much shame was woven into my being. I always had shameful thoughts about myself running my brain and body ragged. I used so many tools to neutralize this shame, but they only helped me keep my head above the drowning level.

Obviously, this shame took root in my being just from the nature of the violence I endured. I think it was easy to allow shame to grow and perpetuate because so much of the world mirrored that I was not enough as a girl, as a woman, as a human.

I do still have moments when I feel vulnerable without that cloak of shame. I feel exposed and yet I realize that I was always the first one to attack myself. Being and sitting with my vulnerability is a worthwhile practice.

There are many layers of vulnerability and just when I get comfortable, another emerges, inviting me to expose more of my heart.

Freedom from shame and old wounds of unforgiveness would not have happened if the seed of wanting forgiveness to happen had never been planted.

Even if it seems impossible for you to experience forgiving someone that harmed you, I encourage you to say, "Someday, I would like to be free from the weight of unforgiveness. Prepare my heart so when the moment arrives, I step into the miracle of unfolding."

A few days later, Angela wrote in her journal:

I felt that my heart space had doubled in size. In my daily prayers I asked God to bring things up so I could let go of even more. I would think of old painful experiences and I forgave myself and others easily. Since I had tackled the biggie in my life, all these other wounds were senseless to hold on to. Sometimes tears accompanied my prayers of forgiveness, but overall, each time I practiced forgiveness, it just got easier and easier.

It seemed pointless to hang on to anything that weighed me down. Forgiveness was my new happy pill and I dosed myself frequently.

* * *

Step completely as a warrior of love
walk with dignity fight for love
the earth is calling all warriors
"Calling All Warriors" -
Thrive Street Choir

2014, AGE 46

A friend recommended that Angela attend a women's retreat. She'd previously participated in survivor retreats, but this one was longer and the location especially appealed to her. The three-day retreat for fifteen women was to be held at a camp in Colorado. The mountains were calling. Most of the attendees slept in their own tents, but she didn't own one, so she had no other choice but to sleep in her car.

The agenda included outdoor cooking, yoga, writing, spiritual nurturing, and self-growth exercises. She was particularly interested in the meditative dance, which promoted well-being and self-reflection. Angela decided to join for the long weekend.

When she arrived, she immediately noticed that the camp was less than a mile from the state highway and only a few miles from the nearest town. It wasn't isolated, which put her mind at ease, knowing she could leave at any time.

It was summertime and the weather was pleasant. On the second evening, after dinner, Angela participated in the reflective dance, listening to acoustic music. Krystal, the group leader spoke and guided the women through the music with thoughts of healing and *visualizing being whole*. She was touched by the music, singing, dancing, and movement of the other participants. She was stirred and filled with emotions and silently wept.

The group leader went to talk to her afterwards, "You were

emotional during the dance; it must have connected with you in a powerful way."

"Yes, it did. This retreat has filled my soul. I'm glad that I came here. It's only the second day, but I've already bonded with some of the women," Angela shared.

"Many people make lifelong friendships. Everyone here feels damaged in some way, and sometimes, an aspect of healing is to witness *and to be* witnessed by others," Krystal told her and smiled. She took a deep breath and continued, "It's all about coming together to share, heal, and celebrate ourselves."

"I'm starting to love myself, even though I've had years of conflicted feelings. Sometimes it is hard to allow myself to be happy," Angela answered.

"Find as many ways as you can to be happy. Then trust it. Is there anything that I can help you with?"

"Not specifically. I think the various activities are spirit nourishing, so it is helping me."

"Most of us here are survivors of abuse. Nobody knows any of your details, and you don't have to tell me anything. I'm curious, what made you want to come to this retreat?"

"I'm here to continue healing and forgiveness."

"Ah, the other 'F' word," Krystal replied with an acknowledging smile.

Angela understood Krystal's reaction. "I'll never be one-hundred percent complete; there's always more ways I can forgive myself and my abuser without rehashing the past," she commented, and Krystal nodded her head with understanding and compassion.

"We are always seeking the truth of our past, aren't we?"

"Yes, and in my experience, it provides freedom. Truth is looking yourself in the eye while owning who you are and who you have been."

"I hope you make progress while you're with us," Krystal replied with empathy.

"I already have. I've had suppressed memories for the longest time, and I didn't like myself and felt a lot of shame. But I'm believing more in myself. For many years, if you would ask me about my self-esteem level, I would say it was a zero. But now it's more than that," Angela remarked.

"It sounds like you've journeyed on a long path of healing. You've been adapting throughout your entire life because of your trauma. It's never done in one leap, but rather thousands of baby steps."

"Maybe a million steps! I've been working on myself *for decades*," Angela responded with a laugh, at ease with teasing herself.

"For me, the hardest thing was to stop daydreaming about a different family, a different history. I spent a lot of time wanting to rewrite a story that couldn't be changed," Krystal revealed.

"It is the same with me. I've longed for a healthier family and a better version of myself," Angela explained.

"I don't know what you've been through, but you seem put together to me," Krystal complimented.

"I'm surprisingly good at being a chameleon and fitting into society. I get along with most people at work, and don't appear too messed up. But I can always tell when somebody else has a history like myself."

"Yes, by necessity, every day we all practice coping in the real world. This retreat is to get away from our daily routine for a while and revitalize yourself so you can have a full life *despite* what happened in your past."

"*Healing is hard work,* and I'm up for the challenge. I'm glad that this retreat provides a great chance for journaling, which is helpful for me," Angela remarked.

Krystal smiled and slowly placed her hand gently on Angela's shoulder, met her eyes, and said, "It takes courage to step out of your daily life to come here."

Angela welcomed the comfort. Krystal added, "We all get to choose to live our life with zeal, because if you don't, then our abuser wins. You can't change the fact that it's part of who you are."

Angela nodded. "I've learned to accept the past because I have no power to change it. My power begins with how I choose to work through it."

"That's true for me too. You are correct, healing is hard work, but life is worth it."

"For me, much of my healing has been centered on understanding my shame and how it's been so woven into my life, so maybe I can once and for all, shed my title, *Queen of Shame.*"

PART 5, 2017, AGE 49

Angela made the decision to move to Colorado and live with a relative in Denver. She worked in a chiropractic and acupuncturist's office and did some house sitting to earn an income, but was reluctant to get another full-time traditional office job.

Throughout the years, working for someone else was stressful, and she sometimes used her job as a coping mechanism. She was able to perform the job adequately, and gained confidence in performing the tasks, but ultimately was unsatisfied. Deep down, she wanted to work for herself and not be defined or identified by a particular job.

Angela became more involved in providing services as a life coach, focusing on the healing arts. These arts included a wide variety of activities such as the emotional freedom technique, guided meditation, brain training, mind-body therapy, Reiki, resiliency methods, journaling, and outdoor activities such as hiking. Although she'd never get rich with this career path, at her core, she knew this is what she was meant to do.

Angela thought back to when her grandfather died and at that time, she felt a sense of relief and in her gut knew that he wouldn't be able to harm another generation. That feeling was unspecific at that time because her memories hadn't yet resurfaced. She wasn't sure why she felt that way, but now it all made sense.

2018, AGE 50

Angela attended a Dance of Universal Peace retreat, and one of the participants was from Cortez, CO, a small town in the southwest corner of the state. After hearing about the area and connecting with the person, she was intrigued. She was concerned about the costs of living on her own, but her new friend offered her a chance to make a fresh start and live together, so she decided to leave Denver and head west.

A few weeks after her TEDx talk in Grand Junction, Angela met with one of the organizers.

"I was grateful for the opportunity to be a presenter," Angela commented.

"It was very impactful," Ashley responded.

"This feels like what I was born to do. I wanted to connect with the audience. I read my poem at the talk and I couldn't open my eyes after I saw several people crying."

"I wanted people to hear your story, but I had no idea how powerful it was going to be," Ashley said with enthusiasm and then added, "I sat back down in my seat and said to myself, 'Now that's a TEDx talk!'"

"Even if you don't have my type of healing to do, everyone has something to heal. I can help others heal and show them that if you step into healing, you are impacting yourself, those around you, and future generations," Angela stated.

"That is so true."

"You know my journey has been long and difficult, and my daughter recently told me that I don't resemble the person I was when she was growing up. She's witnessed the improvement, so I know that my healing has helped someone besides myself."

"I agree, and you're amazing."

"Thanks," Angela responded, knowing she had come such a long way. "Speaking of TED talks, one of my favorites is from Dr. Nadine Burke Harris from a few years ago. Have you seen it?"

"No, what's that about?"

"She discusses adverse childhood experiences and how it affects the person physically, from chronic pain to heart disease and a twenty-year life expectancy reduction."

"Trauma like you experienced?"

"Yes, but it could be physical too. She talks about how severe childhood trauma changes a person's physiology."

"Do you mean physical growth?"

"Yes, but even more importantly, the development of the brain. It can happen when a child experiences a repeated pattern of stress from abuse or neglect. It can also include parents struggling with mental health or substance abuse issues. It has real and tangible effects on the brain development."

"That sounds serious."

"It is. It's beyond a social or mental health crisis. She explains how trauma physically manifests itself in our bodies. I think it explains a lot of my ailments."

"That's something you should continue to talk about at your speaking engagements."

"I will," Angela promised.

"You were also telling me about possibly joining the Colorado Human Trafficking Council. Is that going to happen?" Ashley asked.

"I don't think so. It would be an unpaid position for me, and I can't afford to contribute ten to twelve hours of work per month," Angela answered.

"Are the other members paid?"

"Indirectly, yes. The council is made up of thirty-five people, and as part of their day job, they also attend the meetings, and provide input to the Colorado Department of Public Safety. It's part of their job description, so they are getting paid by their employer."

"Why doesn't the state of Colorado pay you?" Ashley asked.

"State statute doesn't allow the members to be paid directly, so it would be a volunteer position for me, unless I'm financially sponsored by another entity to join."

"You're independent; you don't work for a state agency or large nonprofit."

"Exactly. I'd have to find sponsorship by myself. I would love to be on the council representing survivors, but I just can't do it for free," Angela replied, frustrated.

"How many survivors are on the council?"

"It's usually three to five."

"That's it?" Ashley asked incredulously. "Who are the other thirty people?

"They have other state agencies, law enforcement, prosecutors, NGOs (non-governmental organizations), legal services, victim service providers and academia, all appointed by the governor," Angela answered.

"It's good to have a wide variety of perspectives, but the number of survivors seems too small."

"I agree. But without sponsorship, I can't afford to volunteer my time. I have to concentrate on making a living."

"That's really too bad," Ashley said, feeling dejected and disappointed.

She could see Angela was frustrated, so she decided to change the subject. "The last time we got together it was before your TEDx talk; you said you were journaling about your relationship with God. Have you done more of that?" Ashley asked.

"Yes. For the longest time, I couldn't say the word *God*. In my early days, I would ask myself, *Where the hell were you, God? How could you let humanity get to that point?* I preferred the new age healer's safe concepts, like a universal life force that's bigger than me. They focused on a deep spiritual healing to my moral injury."

"You have a relationship with the God that you've defined, a thread that keeps humanity together. Is that what you mean?"

"Yes, I yelled for help to God, and I've come to develop a deeper relationship. God is willing to go with us anywhere. God is bigger than we can articulate, and that's how I connect with God," Angela explained.

"Sort of in a holistic mystical kind of way?"

"Not exactly, new age toxic positivity doesn't work, either. That tends to only focus on affirmation and disregard the negative. People are sometimes relieved if they only focus on being positive, and they feel they're off the hook and don't need to ask me more questions."

"And hear the difficult answers. But life is both the good and the bad," Ashley added.

"Of course. I do try to have a positive attitude and outlook, but I see the complete picture. I have a better relationship with God than ever. In quiet moments, God has spoken to me."

"Can I pry and ask what was said?"

"Sure," Angela answered with a wry smile. "I've had some profound moments. God had a voice in my head who said, *I never left you*. I can see a giant hand of God cradling me while I was being raped. I'm in the hand of God and I understand that it isn't God's job to make things happen *or not*. God doesn't *right the wrongs.*"

"You're talking about the free will of humans."

"Exactly. It's God's job to hold my hand while it's happening. God didn't orchestrate the bad things that happened to me. I take a lot of comfort from that. It took me a long time to come to that conclusion. It changed my relationship with God, and I'm thankful."

"I think you surprise people with your optimistic attitude," Ashley replied.

"It's true. I'm thankful that I am alive, intelligent, not addicted, look normal and fit in. I'm not bitter. I'm also thankful for the little things, the daily things. Originally, I thought it wouldn't be a life-long battle, but it is. I'm healing all the time, even now."

"And you're still held in the palm of God's hand."

2019, AGE 51

After meeting and working with other survivors, Angela gained as much as she gave. It was an equal balance that provided solace. It also motivated her to be more involved in the movement. Included in her journaling, Angela sometimes wrote poetry. She decided to author a poem to her fellow survivors:

> Roses are red
> Violets are blue
> Love heals they said
> Belonging too
>
> With hammering heart, I whispered
> I'm a survivor just like you
> Overnight I was surrounded
> By a beautiful family that knew

Their radical acceptance would spread
A mysterious sense of belonging too
I didn't know that I needed, I said
to know you, and you, and you
I believe Spirit led
You to me and I to you
Each of you is a sacred thread
In the fabric of my life anew
With a grateful heart I whispered
Thank you

Roses are red
Violets are blue
Love heals they said
Belonging too

* * *

Angela became more involved with survivors and related nonprofits, but less as a recipient and more as a volunteer, and sometimes a paid speaker and consultant. Her time was split between working in the movement and as a life coach in the healing arts. Therapy was always essential and beneficial for her, but it was the healing arts that helped her the most.

Over the years, she attended and presented at many conferences. This work furthered her own healing process by helping others and sharing her story. After working in several different areas of work over her adult life, Angela finally found her place.

The balance between working in the movement and being in a solo practice was challenging and aggravating. Sometimes, NGOs had little or no budget to pay for Angela's speaking responsibilities. Sometimes the travel and related costs exceeded the meager

$500 speaking fees she earned. Not being associated with a specific NGO sometimes left her feeling alone because no one had her back. Working in the movement full-time could be draining, so she continued to stay independent.

Charities, government agencies, and NGOs have good intentions, yet sometimes miss the mark. After all, many of them don't have day-to-day operations managed or reviewed by survivors.

As Angela met more survivors, some common experiences became clear. Some NGOs only scratched the surface when it came to services that survivors needed while others were too focused on religious conversion. After frequently attending conferences and events, she collected her thoughts about what advocates and allies needed to know. She wanted to provide clarity about the survivor's healing journey. One conference prompted an eye-opening discussion.

"Thank you for your presentation," Martha stated with a grateful smile. "We have some time left for questions if that's okay with you."

"Sure," Angela answered. She'd completed her hour and twenty-minute presentation at the Rocky Mountain Human Trafficking Conference.

"You mentioned about halfway through your keynote that you were putting together a letter to advocates and allies. Many of them are in this room. Can you give us some insight to the letter you are writing?" Martha kicked off the question-and-answer portion.

"Yes, I can. First, I want to express gratitude that there are so many caring people working in the movement. At one time I was a victim, just like so many of the people you help. But *I am so much more than that.* You may see clients on the worst day of their life. They may still be physically bruised and recently escaped their situation."

Angela continued, "But that's when we start the journey as a survivor. Don't continue to see us as victims. You may not see us later, when our lives are mostly put back together, or decades later like myself. Don't express sorrow for what we've been through. Don't tell me I *was* brave; it's going to take more years of brave acts to heal."

"Many people I've worked with don't like being called a victim, but there's a whole lot of work to make that transition to survivor," Martha added.

"Yes, and consider that your approach, language and perception of us can be the first time we've been allowed to make choices and see ourselves as more than a victim. It's planting the seed that you already see us as a survivor. It can be our first glimpse of empowerment," Angela replied, receiving the undivided attention of the five hundred people in the hotel conference room.

"Any questions from the audience?" Martha asked.

"Hi, I appreciate this conversation around language. As a survivor leader myself, I cringe when I hear an organization say they've rescued some number of victims last year. What do you think about the word rescue?" asked Nicole, a strong anti-trafficking advocate.

"I hear that! In fact, my letter starts with, 'Please don't use the words rescue or save anymore.' Not in your organization's name or literature as I believe that words impact our mindset. Let me elaborate:

"*Rescue* negates my daily pursuit of freedom. Rescue says I'm not capable of taking a step towards you, yet I ran to you a million times in my mind before taking that literal first step. It also implies that I was waiting around for Superman to swoop in. I had to choose to survive through my ordeal. Don't minimize that fact," Angela told them and she could see several heads nodding in understanding.

"*Rescue* says I'm a charity case. I say I'm resourceful, feisty, and strong! Most of all, rescue says you are the hero. But, I'm the hero of my life. I *need* to be my own hero, to be empowered to persist in the years of recovery ahead," Angela stated with passion, knowing her explanation could influence the audience.

Angela continued her explanation packed with powerful meaning, "*Rescue* says my hands and feet were bound; your eyes can't see the bondage that held me. Less than five percent of the time have I been literally bound. The word *save* limits my ability to participate in my freedom. *Save* removes my choice to respond to your outreach."

"*Save* says I'm helpless," Angela explained with emphasis and some allies saw strength in a survivor for the first time. She saw in their faces a yearning for more. She sensed their hearts were in the right place and filled with the desire to be more impactful with their clients, so she decided to continue, "*Save* implies a happily-ever-after magical ending. We all know that's not usually true."

"That makes sense. I'm hearing from you that it doesn't end when the exploitation stops, and allies need to be there for the long journey afterwards," Martha commented.

"Exactly," Angela agreed. "Our struggles belong to us. We're the ones who have to live with it. It's not your story. We constantly work to achieve freedom from our violent oppression. My pursuit of freedom didn't end when the trafficking stopped."

"Do you mean that you were worried about losing your freedom and being trafficked again?" Chris asked, who was the founder of a well-established anti-human trafficking nonprofit.

"In my case, no, although that's a real concern for some. Anyone with a traumatic history like mine is vulnerable to further exploitation. Our mind, heart, and spirit must also be free from our past experiences. That is not an easy task or a quick one. I still fight that battle, even decades later."

"You want to be independent and in control of your life," Martha commented.

"Yes, and more," Angela added. "I want the allies to appreciate the greater percent of my lived experience. I need words and images that provoke respect, not pity or sympathy. Show me how dignity looks on me.

"I can always tell an older organization because it's not the way survivors have asked to be represented. Those images of me bruised and beaten may have been true before I was free. The truth many don't want to see is that during most of my captivity, *I looked just like you*. That likeness of me bound with chains. Please don't use it. Sensationalized large metal chains have never been wrapped around me.

"The photos of me behind bars or with ropes around my wrists are metaphors we don't use anymore. I've not been locked in a cage with a key that you held. Please don't show me naked or in the shadows. If we mislead with images and words, my community will never see me living in their midst. Liberate me by showing the world that I look like you," Angela spoke with zeal and was on a roll. The audience was captivated, and some nodded their head with recognition that they were sometimes off the mark in understanding the breadth of what survivors needed so they could continue their life.

"As I rebuild my life, celebrate each step of that, please. Show the world my smile. And when my story can help prevent, educate, or inform, please share my story, with my permission. I am not talking about the sordid, degrading details of my horror. This harms everyone.

"Give the hero's journey to me, no matter my age. The triumphant survivor learning to live and love. That's what all survivors need. We want to emphasize the courageous actions that lead us to new levels of freedom. The flame of hope that I keep feeding.

The resilience I exercise to undo the impact of force, fraud, and coercion."

"That is really powerful," Martha told her and then looked at the audience.

"Don't get me wrong, we need all of you," Angela reiterated. "Many times, you are a true lifeline. Also, put a survivor on your board of directors. Allow them to review your protocols. Hire them to work in the organization. And most importantly, *actually listen to them.*"

"Let me comment on other words I agree with, such as identified, recovered, exit, escape, and self-rescue. The images I agree with will reflect human strength, resiliency, and triumph."

Ask me about my current life, which reflects post-traumatic growth, love, and security. Ask not if I'm happy, but what brings me happiness. Ask me about my first snorkeling adventure because I survived so I could experience child-like joy that induced giggles and tears," Angela replied. She was unstoppable.

"Each survivor is unique and at a different point in their healing. As a child, I needed help to exit, just like I needed someone to teach me how to ride my bike. Empower me to be my own hero by walking beside me. Teach me to make choices of my own. Show me how to develop my sense of self. Please don't say that you rescued or saved me; then I owe you, and I've paid enough already. Please don't use my story or photo without permission to raise money for I don't owe you. Especially if I am a minor, can you see how re-exploitive this is for me?" Angela asked the audience and sensed that she was getting through to them.

"Many of us survivors are on a financial edge. We have an unhealthy relationship with money. We were so used to having our bodies exchanged for money that cash feels dirty. Many of us that were exploited haven't had the best education or have problems keeping a job. I am grateful that you pray for me, but also be aware that there are immediate and practical needs like paying the rent or childcare. Don't immediately try to convert me to your religion, if I want to, I'll come on my own terms."

"It sounds like you want independence and to be empowered to take control of your life," Martha concluded.

"Yes, you get it!" Angela exclaimed with a smile. "Empower me to be my own hero by walking beside me. That's where you can play a vital role."

"You want to be our peer, not a pity case," Martha added.

"Yes. My goal is to heal completely so when I walk into the room, no one knows I'm here as a survivor. I don't want my trauma to define me, and I don't want to be noticed for that. When I focus on healing, I have hope for humanity even though I have seen the worst in people. If I can heal, everyone else can, including the perpetrators," Angela continued.

"Ask me about how I live and love. Ask me about my river trips in stunning desert canyons because I'm worthy of a whitewater adventure. In these questions, you'll discover I'm much more like you than you've imagined. This movement needs you and me. Let's remind everyone of my ability *to rise beyond freedom*."

* * *

Whoa, yes, I am wise
But it's wisdom born of pain
Yes, I've paid the price
But look how much I gained
If I have to I can do anything
I am strong (strong)
I am invincible (invincible)
I am woman
"I am Woman" - Helen Reddy

ROBIN'S RESTAURANT
SALIDA, CO, DECEMBER 19, 2021

The following is an except of the audio recordings the author conducted with Angela:

Author: Given everything you've gone through, how do you have, *or do you have,* a positive view on humanity when you've seen the worst?

Angela: When I focus on healing, I have hope for humanity.

Author: That makes sense.

Angela: Even with the flashbacks I've had in the last couple weeks, ugh. It made me sick to my stomach. The only thing that pulls me out of that lack of hope is when I come back to: If I can heal, everybody can heal, perpetrators can heal, people in prison can heal, my family can choose to heal.

Angela: I talk about being in a victim lens for a lot of my life. As long as I saw myself as a victim, I was going to create a lot of scenarios where I was victimized. That was a big part of my self-agency, moving away from that story.

Angela: I don't want the trauma to be evident. You know when you go to a conference and they have a meet and greet? I don't want to be the person that enters the room and everyone says, "Oh, the survivor arrived, we know that she's here!" I want to come in and have them ask, "Is the survivor here yet?"

Author: The goal is normalcy, whatever that phrase means.

Author: I think you have a greater, deeper appreciation, thankfulness, gratefulness than the average person, I get a sense.

Angela: I think that people who have been the most harmed, if we are given the space to heal, we'll be the leaders in helping other people, giving them permission to heal.

Author: What are you thankful for?

Angela: I've had countless people who have had more faith in me than myself. And that's necessary.

Author: That's a testament of them seeing you as you are.

Angela: Well, I thought a monster was living inside me!

Author: Right, so why would you want to look inside?

Angela: They saw somebody who had much more potential than I could ever see myself as. I don't have regret for the choices I've made and I've been able to make meaning out of a lot of it, and it's always been beneficial to me.

Angela: Secondly, I want it to benefit anybody that sees it, hears it, or reads about it. It does feel like this is why I was born. To interrupt it happening in my family, to be the person that asks, "Is this really what we want our family legacy to be?" It's not what I want it to be. I think that most families have that person, at least I hope that they do. I hope there's somebody who stands up and says, "No, we're not going to do this anymore."

Author: That was part of your TEDx talk.

Angela: Yes, and it felt like it was what *I was born to do.*

Author: Wow. Were you filled up emotionally? That was only a couple of years ago, and you've had this long journey to get to that TEDx talk moment. Did your journey feel like it had a purpose?

Angela: Absolutely, purpose is woven into that. Same with the blogs, conference teaching, and doing one-on-one education. All of that helps me fill up my purpose and redeem some of my lived experience.

Author: You said, "This is what I was meant to do." What is *that*?

Angela: Telling my story and impacting the audience. I had to close my eyes when I read that poem because people were crying. To go from that and end it by talking about forgiveness and healing. I had a smile on my face. It did what I wanted it to do.

Author: What did you want the audience to get out of it?

Angela: What I want with everything is for people to say, "I don't have to heal from *that*, but I have to heal from *this*."

Author: Meaning, I have healing to do, and hearing your story will help with my own healing? Is that right?

Angela: Yes

Author: So, that ties into my next question. What do you want the reader to get out of your chapter?

Angela: The hard things that you've experienced in your life. If you dive into addiction, you haven't done anyone any favors, least of all yourself. But if you can step into healing, you're impacting future generations. You're impacting the people that are *around you right now*. You're impacting yourself. If your pet of twenty years has died and you're broken up over it, then *heal that shit up*.

Author: Work on it, whatever it is.

Angela: It might be like a stubbed toe compared to being trafficked, but your stubbed toe matters. Whatever the brokenness that's in your heart, and everybody's got some pain, whatever it is, look at, address it, do take action on it. You and your pain matter just as much as me and my pain. And if it doesn't take an entire lifetime to heal . . .

Author and Angela simultaneously: **All the better.**

* * *

Find out more about Angela Rae Clark:

Rise Beyond Freedom
Mind*Body*Energy Coach
Writer & Speaker

To find out more about Angela and her forthcoming book, go to:

www.risebeyondfreedom.com

* * *

To watch Angela Rae Clarks TEDx talk in Grand Junction, CO, go to:

https://www.ted.com/talks/angela_rae_clark_what_to_do_after_metoo

To watch Dr. Nadine Burke Harris TED talk, go to:

https://www.ted.com/talks/nadine_burke_harris_how_childhood_trauma_affects_health_across_a_lifetime

4
FILLING THE SILENCE

JESSICA JOY

If I should speak then let it be
Of the grace that is greater than all my sin
Of when justice was served and where mercy wins
Of the kindness of Jesus that draws me in
Oh to tell you my story is to tell of Him
"My Story" - Big Daddy Weave

PART 1, RIDGEWAY, CO,
SEPTEMBER 2021, AGE 40

Thwack! That feels good. Although my shoulders are aching, I enjoy the soreness that results from demanding work. Physical and manual work suits this farm girl. The axe rises once again and thrusts downward without trouble, splitting another piece of wood. In less than an hour, fifty split pieces now lay piled on the ground.

The sun is shining, and it's a beautiful day in the Colorado mountains, with the cobalt sky going on forever. But more wood is needed, so don't let the warm autumn day fool you; winter is coming.

My mind is blank and my spirit is at peace while I'm chopping wood. Although a touch over forty years old, my five-foot-ten-inch frame helps me bring down enough force for the axe to mercilessly split another piece of wood. A frail female I am not. Thwack!

Chopping wood provides purpose and a chance to tithe my time to my parents. They don't fully understand my life over the past twenty years, as it's hard for them to think deeply about it, which is understandable. Why would they want to know every sordid detail? Why upset them any further?

This wood will eventually keep my parents' house warm throughout the winter. The goal is to chop five cords by the end of the month. A bead of sweat drips down my face and I'm no longer cold in the crisp morning air.

The noise is minimal, except for the sound of the axe striking wood and hitting the ground. I finally accept the silence. There's no longer an instinctual and habitual need to fill the silence, for I'm content. I'm busy and have a great relationship with my parents and I live on a mere few thousand dollars a year. Life is simpler.

Thwack! The sound fills the air as I split another piece of pine. The tree isn't destroyed by chopping it into little pieces. Instead, it's converting stored energy into life-giving heat. I gaze at the pile of chopped wood and see pieces of a puzzle. That's like all of us. Someone's story isn't just one piece. More important than understanding the pieces of one's life is the insight to see how it all fits together.

A thousand-piece jigsaw puzzle is the best way to describe me. I'm not just one piece or one experience. I'm more than the sum of the parts, an amalgamation of pieces put together in a particular order. The "why" part is just as important as the "what."

Until you understand all the pieces and how they fit together, you won't be able to see the complete puzzle. But my story isn't only about me.

The story exposes what's going on in our world. My motivation to tell my story isn't to talk about me, but to reveal our culture and society. To understand me is to see the bigger picture. My only possessions are experiences and memories and I freely share them with you.

Only by the grace of God, I'm not dead or hooked on drugs. That's a miracle, touched by the hand of God. It's the simpleness of chopping wood in solitude that allows my reflection and understanding.

As a child, I never imagined how many roads I'd travel to get to this farm in a small Colorado mountain town. It's never too late to rebuild your life and come back to God. There's no way to avoid the struggle and if I can remake my life, so can anyone else.

You're in for a wild ride, so sit down and get comfortable and allow me to introduce myself. My name is Jessica, and I'll be your tour guide.

PART 2, 6,368 DAYS EARLIER, APRIL 10, 2004, EASTER SUNDAY, ESTES PARK, CO, AGE 23

It's cold; very cold. How can it be this cold inside the apartment? I'm shivering underneath my blankets, and I can see my breath. How cold does it have to be to see your breath? There's no incentive to get out of bed and get ready for work as a housekeeper at the YMCA of the Rockies. It's clearly a job, not a career, but it does help pay the bills.

My calling and real work is as an unpaid youth pastor at the local church, which translates to a lot of demanding work without any pay. Therefore, it's necessary to cobble together several part-time jobs to cover my expenses. A tourist town like Estes Park is filled with short-term service industry jobs, mostly paying minimum wage, which explains the high turnover and instability of the workforce.

Looking back, how very different my life was a few months ago. Before moving to Estes Park, I was a youth pastor in Brighton, CO, at a much larger church earning $40,000 annually and running several programs. That job started when I was only nineteen years old. That's noticeably young, although I had experience in youth ministries for many years through my own church in Cedaredge, CO where my father was the pastor.

My dad was a go-getter at church, for he saw potential opportunities where others saw nothing. He had the vision to get things done, and I followed in his path. I grew up loving Jesus passionately and couldn't imagine my life without Him. When it came to church, I was all in, so it was only natural to become a youth minister as a young adult.

I helped make the youth program a success, growing the group from seven to almost ninety kids. I still can't figure out how I was hired at only nineteen, although I was sure being the daughter of a successful pastor factored into the hiring process. Somehow, they assumed I'd already graduated from a local Bible college because I completed a few seminary courses. I jumped at the $40,000 salary, big bucks for someone barely out of high school. Months into the job, the pastor finally asked about my age, shocked to learn I was only a year older than some of the ministry participants.

I learned right away how to spend my paycheck. As fast as the money came in, it went out just as quickly, anywhere and everywhere. It was easy to spend and hard to keep track of. The first purchase was a car, a Kia Rio, demonstrating my practical side, surprised that my impulsive side didn't win out with something flashier. My increase in cash flow didn't correlate with an increase in maturity or a better decision process. Youth and money created easy opportunities to make mistakes.

I considered myself pretty special, earning a high salary at such an early age. A few years into the job, I drove to a youth conference and crashed into a lamp post. *That* wasn't special. I could make up an excuse and tell you that the parking lot was crowded, and I swerved to avoid hitting a young mother pushing a baby carriage, but that'd be a lie. I was just being stupid.

It wasn't long after the accident that the pastor decided my time was up. But luckily, I networked over my employment time, while touring Colorado to talk to various groups about the True Love Waits program, which promotes abstinence and purity before marriage. When my job at the Brighton church ended, a friend referred me to an opening at a church in Estes Park, my present nonpaying youth minister job.

Besides working as a housekeeper, I'm also the catering supervisor for the Stanley Hotel, but I'm always out of money. Estes Park is the eastern gateway to Rocky Mountain National Park, a small tourist town with a population of about 5,500 people and sits 7,522 feet above sea level. Springtime is weeks away, and it's still cold and snowy with this morning's temperature at a blustery ten degrees.

I drag myself out of bed and run to the shower, waiting forever for the water to get hot. Already inside the shower are my dishes and clothes. I must find creative ways to save time and money, so I wash myself, the dishes, and clothes with Palmolive soap.

The warm water heating my body feels good. Why buy expensive shampoo when you can use dish soap?

I'm unhappy working in Estes Park and living paycheck to paycheck. I haven't made many friends either, and I hardly ever see my parents. But I try to refocus on the ministry at church. I'm doing all of this for you, God. I'm a martyr for you. I should be happy to bear the cross, but I am starting to wonder, *Did you abandon me?* I'm performing important work, serving the church and my community as a youth minister. I don't want much, but if you could help me afford a little heat so I don't freeze to death during the night, it would be nice.

Honestly, I'm frustrated with you, God. I need to work at least two jobs, begging my boss for more hours at minimum wage. But that's not the worst part.

I had to work during Christmas week since it's a busy time in the tourist town. It was horrible being away from my parents, talking to them on the phone instead of being at home. How can I call myself a true Christian if I'm working instead of being in church to celebrate the birth of Your Son?

It's happening again because I need to work on Easter, the most important day of the church year. I'm supposed to be thinking about your resurrection, not making sure the food for brunch is properly displayed and kept warm.

But it's one of the busiest weeks at the Stanley Hotel, catering to wealthy visitors since July 4, 1909. I'm angry that I'm required to work on Easter. I want to serve and worship you, Lord, but you are making it difficult. Why am I in this predicament? Why am I forced to choose between making my rent payment, let alone my heating bill, verses going to church to worship you? It's not fair.

18 HOURS LATER

I'm the designated driver for several coworkers; we've gone to a local's bar after our long sixteen-hour shift. It's almost midnight and my Kia Rio will be ice cold. I head to the far-away parking lot to start the car and warm it up before driving them home from the local bar. I'd rather go to bed, but it's my mission to serve others, so like I've done before, I agree to drive everyone home even though I'm grumpy.

About twelve hours ago, I looked at my watch and recognized the time as when I should be arriving at church for the Easter service. Yet instead, I was busting my butt getting a shrimp cocktail put together for a crowd of tourists.

I'd rather do Your work, not managing an assembly line for gluttonous visitors. I admit that I'm not a happy person right now. Have You forgotten about me? I realize there are lots of problems in the world, and I know there are other people who need you more, God, who are suffering more, but it would be nice if you could help me out a little bit.

Why is my life going in this direction? God, why am I working at a hotel with a bunch of nonbelievers instead of serving you full time? Am I too shortsighted to see that I don't need a full-time paycheck to do Your work?

I approach my car and involuntarily shiver from the cold, fumbling with the keys because it's so dark. For a brief second, I hear footsteps approach me, but before I have a chance to turn around, hands grab my head and shoulder and I'm slammed into the car's roof, right where it meets the top of the door. I immediately wonder who's attacking me and what's going on.

But then my thoughts are instantly replaced with searing pain and I see stars. There's a cut on my forehead just below my hairline. I notice a warm liquid sensation on my face. It seeps into my eyes; it's my own blood, and I'm lying on the pavement. My head is aching, and my brain is processing everything in slow motion. I'm dazed and squint to see more clearly but that only makes my head hurt worse.

The sound of a belt buckle opening tightens my stomach. A nervous sweat makes me feel even colder, and the blood is hot on my face and neck. He is going to attack me. I look to my left and see underneath my car. To my right, my eyes are parallel with the snow, which is starting to melt from the warmth of my own blood.

He's taking his pants off. Is he going to rape me? Why does he want to rape me? Did I flirt inappropriately with any men tonight? No, I've not given any signals to anyone. Am I wearing a short skirt? No. Am I showing too much cleavage? No, you can hardly see anything. I'm never going to win a beauty contest, so why does he want to rape me?

The sound of his Cricket ringtone rattles and permeates the quiet night air. My brain is trying to process his actions. There's someone on the other end of that cellphone who has no idea what's happening on this side. He doesn't answer the phone, and that damn sound won't stop as it's hard-wired into my brain.

Is this really happening to me? I'm paralyzed, I can't move, I can't scream, I can't fight him off, and I don't know what to do!

This cannot be reality. Is he really going to have sex with me on the cold pavement in an empty parking lot? I try to scream, but the sound is in my head and nothing comes out of my mouth. Why is he doing this to me and why can't I fight back?

I feel pressure on my body, and I get a sick feeling when he enters me. It's revolting and dirty. I'm feeling horrified and soiled. There's a certain kind of girl who attracts this type of man, *but I'm not that girl.*

I think back to giving presentations about purity. This is impure. I preach that sex occurs in the context of love and marriage. Is this what sex is going to be like on my wedding night? My mind is running one hundred miles per hour, going around in circles. I can't complete a thought. I just know that this can't be happening to me.

He gets off me; I see his face, but I don't recognize him. The parking lot is empty, so who's going to help me? No one. The harsh reality sinks in. No one is coming to save me and I'm alone.

This monster has taken something from me. I'm thinking a thousand different thoughts, but I can't process any of them because I am *so damn cold*. I keep screaming in my head that I'm the good girl. I'm the one who talks about purity. I never talk about rape and I'm not the kind of girl who gets raped in a cold dark parking lot on Easter Sunday. I'm not that girl.

He's done and remains silent and doesn't offer any help. He slowly walks away and leaves me half-naked, yet fully exposed. I rage against the reality of the situation. This is *not* the plan for my life.

I try to convince myself that I slipped on the ice and hit my head on the ground. After a few minutes, I pull myself off the pavement and drag myself into the car, which is now warm. I can't let my friends see me, so I drive the two miles back to my apartment.

But deep down inside, I know the truth, and that cold hard truth is this: You'll find my dignity left for dead on the pavement.

* * *

"Monsters are real, and ghosts are real too. They live inside us, and sometimes, they win."

- Stephen King, The Shining

(Legend has it that Stephen King was inspired to write *The Shining* after he and his wife spent a night at Stanley Hotel in Estes Park, CO in 1974.)

* * *

After that horrible night, I cried in my apartment until daylight. I took several long showers in an attempt to wash the filth from my body and soul, hoping that the memory and pain would go down the drain. It didn't.

I am so alone. I'm always so alone. I don't know what to do, and I don't want to talk to anyone. Why would I want to relive that experience? Why would I want anyone else to know what I went through? The pain from the rape hurts deep inside, down to my soul, so why would I want to advertise it to anyone else? This has been the worst time in my life. He stole my virginity, acted like an animal, and treated me as if I weren't human. I was nothing but a means to an end for him.

A few days after the rape, a neighbor notices how distraught I am. She is genuinely concerned and presses me. I can't keep my secret, so I break down and tell her. She convinces me to go to the doctor, but any evidence that the police could use is long gone. I eventually take an STD and pregnancy test. And although I know it's wrong and goes against everything I believe in, if I'm pregnant from this monster, I will abort his demon child. Luckily, I did not get pregnant, and he didn't give me any diseases.

The hardest part of the aftermath is telling my dad about what happened. At first, I wasn't going to tell anyone in my family. But a week after the rape, I am scheduled to speak at the YMCA of the Rockies conference center, about fifteen minutes from my apartment. A few hundred Christian teenagers are on spring break and staying the week at the mountain facility.

I muster enough strength to get myself on stage. But that accomplishment is short-lived because ten minutes into my talk about purity and waiting for marriage, *my reality* hits me. Hard.

The violation, the shame, and the way he degraded me were overwhelming. I start to shake, and I'm under duress. My throat becomes dry, my heart pounds in my chest, and I have difficulty putting together coherent sentences, even though I've given that presentation many times before. Just when I think it couldn't get worse, I lose control of my body and pee in my pants.

This only compounds my embarrassment, and I go into a complete meltdown. My body starts twitching and shaking, and I think I am having a seizure as I leave the stage. When my dad calls a few days later to ask me how the conference went, I can't hold back any longer and I tell him everything. I hear the hurt in his voice, and I blame myself for causing him pain.

* * *

Two months later, I'm traumatized again when my rapist applies for and starts working at the Stanley Hotel. It is shocking to see him, and it gets worse. He recognizes me and talks to me like I'm his girlfriend! There isn't any remorse on his face, and he treats me like his actions are normal. Was he unaware of the damage he'd caused, or did he simply not care?

It never entered my mind that I might see him again, but I should have known that it'd be likely to cross paths in such a small town. The last thing I expected was to engage in casual conversation with my tormentor. For someone who talks a lot, I was left speechless.

Does he really believe we have a relationship? He has the audacity to hope I am pregnant to perpetuate his family lineage. What is he talking about? I almost throw up from the disgusting and gross images that he puts in my mind. Then he leaves to complete his application with human resources. I'm dumbfounded. How can I work in this town any longer?

I need advice, and I talk to my aunt in Oklahoma. She convinces me to go to the police. They open a case and take my statement, but because so much time had passed, there isn't enough evidence to make an arrest. I can't take it any longer, and that's when I know I have to leave.

1 MONTH LATER

My future is scary, but I'm glad to be getting out of this godforsaken town and heading south to Colorado Springs. Dad will arrive soon to help move my stuff out of this dingy apartment. I cringe knowing that it'll be the first time I've seen him since I was raped. It's difficult to say that word in my head, and even more painful to say it aloud.

How do I face my father after I've been raped? The look in his eyes, what will it tell me? He may not say anything, but he must feel differently about me. It's going to be awkward. Will he look at me with pity? Shame? Or maybe disgust? Whatever he thinks, my mind has already gone there. It's the end of an era; I'm no longer his innocent little girl.

From our phone conversations, he noticed my waning interest in another youth minister job. He's already told me that it's okay to find another line of employment. Why isn't he encouraging me to continue working in the ministry, as he has done his entire adult life? That's all I know, so what will I do now?

I'm relieved to lose the obligation, but at the same time, I wonder why he's given his blessing for me to quit the ministry. Is he allowing me to quit the church too? And quit on God? I don't know whether to feel unburdened or petrified about quitting on God.

I'm still not handling it well, and don't understand why this happened to me. I have emotions ranging from stress to sadness to shame. But it's anger that's dominating my mind and heart.

I'm angry with my rapist, myself, and more importantly, *I'm angry with God.* The anger gets stronger with each passing day.

I was dedicated to God and to the ministry. I enjoyed what I was doing and delivering his message of purity and love to teenagers was fulfilling. It was my godly mission. I wanted to positively influence their lives and knew it was my calling. How can I be a youth minister now that I'm a fraud? Who would want me now? My life came to a crashing halt because God allowed this man to destroy me. *Is this how You treat your best followers?*

So, here I am in the parking area behind my small apartment complex, waiting for my dad to arrive and help load my stuff into his van. It's three o'clock in the afternoon and ominous thunder clouds are beginning to form overhead, rolling in over the mountains. It's the perfect message from God about my life: Dark clouds with a storm coming.

I'm no longer wife material. Why would a future husband want to make love to someone who's been raped? I'm damaged and soiled goods so I vow not to be that vulnerable again.

My only choice is to protect my heart. I cannot let anyone else hurt me like I've been over these past couple of months. If I'm to go on, then I must turn my heart to stone. I can't let anything or anyone crack the armor and get to my tender flesh. It's going to be like a cinder block.

There's one fewer box that my dad will need to move. I take the long and lonely walk towards the dumpster at the edge of the parking lot. The heavy box contains a variety of Christian books, some of which I've cherished since childhood. Many of those books I've read several times, and they fundamentally shaped my love for Jesus. But no more. What good are they now?

I lift the heavy box onto the top of the dumpster and in one swooping motion, the box with my most important books over the last twenty years falls to the bottom, making a loud, clanking noise that echoes through my mind and my heart. I'm done. And in the shadows behind the dumpster, I fail to notice the devil is smiling.

* * *

"For what is a man profited, if he shall gain the whole world, and lose his own soul?"

- Matthew 16:26

PART 3, FEBRUARY 14, 2005, AGE 24

"What did Meghan tell you?"

"What do you think?" Donna asks me.

"I was told to fire her. She can't come to work, sporting a new hickey for the world to see, now can she?" I answer with a sarcastic grin, sitting with perfect posture in the chair across from Donna's desk.

I've been working for several months at the Christian-based Glen Eyrie Castle and Conference Center in Colorado Springs. I've utilized the skills I learned at the Stanley Hotel and applied them here, working my way up to become the youngest catering manager at the facility. I was told by my supervisor to fire Meghan, a young lady on my staff. She didn't take it well and immediately marched into Donna's office, the human resources manager.

"I agree that the result of Meghan's behavior does not reflect Glen Eyrie's values and image. But she also had some stories to tell about you," Donna answers.

"About me? Do you want to check for hickeys?" I quickly retort and pull down my collar to reveal my neck and clavicle. I confidently lean back in the chair, daring her to find any mark of promiscuity.

236

"No, it's not that, but she said it's well known among the staff that you're a party girl," Donna counters.

"Is that so?" I scoff back at her. "What I do on my time is my own business, as long as I don't come to work showing the sign of the beast, right?" I flippantly ask.

"Yes, I understand that. What you do on your own time is your personal business, but we host a lot of visitors, and we certainly don't want them getting the wrong impression about the people we hire, and the morals we believe in," Donna points out, giving me the *"mom"* lecture.

"I've done nothing to embarrass this organization," I snap back in frustration. "Why am I suddenly being judged? Meghan is the one we should be talking about."

"Perhaps Meghan is retaliating for being let go, but the Glen Eyrie has been around a long time and our actions should reflect our thankfulness for God, as you know," Donna declares. She merely wants me to agree so the conversation will end, but I'm not going to give her the satisfaction.

"Thankfulness? What has God done for you?" I ask angrily, pointing my finger directly at Donna, surprising her with my aggressiveness.

"I don't know what you mean, however . . ."

I interrupt before she can finish her sentence and say, "Where was your God last summer?" I ask with purpose and a rising decibel level. Although Donna's office door is closed, it's flimsy enough so a loud voice can easily be heard by everyone in the small office area.

Knowing that, I continue, "Your husband is dead, and you have to raise the kids on your own. What kind of God leaves a good Christian woman like yourself with five young children? Or maybe you're not *that good*, and this is your punishment?" I spit out the stinging words.

I want to hurt her and inflict pain. My cruelty feels satisfying and the look on her face tells me it's working. I smile on the outside and then deliver the knockout blow, "What was he really doing on his mission trip? Maybe *he deserved it.*"

"That's a horrible thing to say," Donna answers and starts crying, her grief rising to the surface. I successfully redirected the conversation.

"Perhaps," I concede. "Why don't you ask your God?"

"God is here to give me strength. Yes, it's been difficult since he passed away," Donna admits.

"Difficult? Of course, it's been difficult. I bet you're glad you're such a strong woman, because God knows you can handle the burden," I retort with sarcasm. "You're so lucky to be a faithful Christian, don't ya think?" I ask. I was on a roll, and there was no stopping me.

Without giving her a chance to speak, I ask, "How could it possibly be anything other than difficult? You're lecturing me about Christian values on Valentine's Day of all days? The day you're all alone? Do you think another man is going to drop in from the sky and become your husband and a father to those kids?"

"Well, I . . ." Donna tries to respond.

"Don't you understand what's going on? God has turned on you, and you're too stupid to notice," I growl at her with a razor-sharp tone.

I'm pleased to put her in her place and knock her down a peg. In that moment, I hate her for looking down at me, sneering at me with her "holier than thou" attitude. Who is she to tell me about Christian values when she can't see the truth in front of her eyes? God screwed her over, and I'm in disbelief that she is still faithful to Him.

Tears drip from her eyes and Donna grabs a tissue. For a moment, I feel sorry for her and thought about apologizing.

I almost reach out my hand to hold hers to provide some comfort. But no, I decide against it. I'm no longer a nice girl.

She deserves to hear my truth. This conversation is over, so I spring out of the chair, roughly open the door, and walk out. I can see the nosey employees trying to look busy in their cubicles, but I don't care. I know what's real and I'm not blinded by fairy tales like these fools and I certainly won't give them the satisfaction of making eye contact. I am planning to quit and go work at the Broadmoor Hotel anyway.

LATER THAT EVENING

"Leah, are you ready to party?" I ask as we approach the entrance to the dance club, hearing the *thump* from the bass pumping out the music. It starts to match the rhythm of my heartbeat. Leah is a friend I grew up with who now lives in Colorado Springs and is a law enforcement consultant.

It is cold outside, but I'm wearing a flimsy and revealing dress. I lost twenty pounds since leaving Estes Park, doing as much as I could with my limited natural beauty. It was Valentine's evening, and the last thing I want to see are happy couples, so I am hoping that the people partying in this nightclub are single and won't be looking for love.

I know what the men will be looking for since I've been to this place several times before. The club offers a lady's drink special so we order a couple. I guzzle mine immediately and Leah rolls her eyes, for she knows what is likely to happen this evening. She is my wing woman, making sure I don't hook up with an ugly guy.

It was great to reconnect with Leah when I moved here a few months ago. When we were growing up, she was involved with the church and dedicated like I was. While in college, Leah backed away from the faith and I punished her for it. I cut her out of my life with my righteous attitude for several years.

Now that we're friends again, I apologized and admitted that she was right and that I needed to loosen up. Today, it's my friends from the ministry that I've abandoned. The tables have turned with Leah because now I'm the rebellious one. She's my clubbing pal and I enjoy shocking her with my new attitude and behavior. Her silence and inability to tell me 'no' only encourages me.

As I finish my third drink, I recognize a song that I like and head towards the dance floor. It doesn't matter if anyone is dancing with me or not. I gyrate enough moves and get the attention of several men in the night club. It works every time; *men are such simple creatures.*

After sending the clear message that I'm ready, willing and able, I know it won't take long for a random guy to approach me. I'm sober enough to determine if he is good looking or not.

A Brad Pitt lookalike heads towards me and begins dancing about twenty feet away. I see him through the crowd, slowly making his way next to me. Just as I expect, our eyes lock briefly, confirming the bee's attraction to my honey.

A few seconds later, he's dancing directly in front of me, so I deliver a mischievous smile and twirl around, letting him admire my body as it grooves to the pulsing music. He says something to me, but I can't understand it because the music is so loud. He gestures with his hand as if he's taking a drink; I nod and follow him to the bar area. When we get there, it is slightly less noisy, and he asks, "What are you having?"

You, I think to myself, but instead, tell him I'd like a Long Island iced tea. He yells to the bartender to order our drinks. I'm pleased that he is spending money on me. I can feel his eyes scoping me out, deciding if I'm worth his trouble. I move, ever so slightly towards him, flash a slow flirty smile, and tell him my name.

"Jessica, you've got some good moves out there," he tells me. Good, our conversation isn't going to go deep.

"Yeah, I've got all kinds of good moves," I naughtily reply to him. He hands me the drink and I suck down my concoction like a pro as I transition from being buzzed to intoxicated. He quickly orders me another drink, and I smile back with glassy eyes.

"Did you come here alone," he asks harmlessly, but I know there is nothing innocent in his question.

I don't see Leah anywhere and no longer care, "I came with a friend, but I am hoping to leave with a new friend," I tell him and playfully touch his hair. He and I know exactly where this is headed. I've got his attention now if you know what I mean.

He nods to the bartender, and points to my empty glass. The loud music makes it difficult to have a meaningful conversation, which is why I often go dancing. A few minutes later my drink is received and consumed.

"Why don't we get out of here?" he suggests. "We can continue this party back at my place. What do you say?"

"Sure, that sounds great," I answer. "I'm a little too tipsy to drive."

"I'll drive," he tells me. I have no clue how much he's consumed, and I don't care if we get to his place safely. We walk to the parking lot and get into his BMW; he's making a good impression. We don't say much during the ride to his apartment, which was fine with me and about ten minutes later I follow him up the stairs to his second-floor home.

"Do you want a beer?" he asks while going into the refrigerator, grabbing two Coronas. I answer by sticking my hand out, and he opens the bottle and gives it to me. I gulp half of it in one swig even though I don't like beer.

I'm drunk, but nevertheless, I will be in control of the situation. I'm going to have sex tonight, but it is going to be my way, not his. I am going to *use him*. I am going to *rape him* so he'll pay for what was done to me. Being in control will ensure that I'm not hurt again.

I've lost track of the number of guys I've slept with since moving back to Colorado Springs. I don't want to know their names or phone numbers, and I don't want to see them again. I only want to use them more than they've used me. It's that simple.

He smiles and I silently return the gesture. I don't want small talk, and I don't care what he does for a living. I don't want to know him *at all*. I'm doing the using; I have the upper hand. I gulp the rest of my beer and slam the bottle down a little too hard on the counter, and smirk at my clumsiness. He doesn't react at all.

He looks at me and I know he won't need any further encouragement. He steps closer, grabs my shoulder, and starts to unzip the back of my dress. Next, he easily unclasps my bra while I'm working to unbutton his shirt. You know what happens next.

Afterwards, I'm lying on my back staring at the ceiling and I realize that we never kissed. I prefer it that way. I don't want to be intimate.

* * *

A few weeks later, I'm downtown and walk by a bunch of free news and magazine racks. There's *The Onion*, real estate listings, and small independent local newspapers, but it's the entertainment magazine that has me intrigued. My eyes zoom in on the advertisement in all capitalized letters: "ESCORT SERVICES."

I'm doing it all wrong! I've been trying to make men pay these past few months. But instead, they're getting sex for free. What am I thinking? This is completely backwards. Becoming an escort would guarantee that men will pay with cold hard cash.

I'm so intrigued by the advertisement that I set up an interview for the following week. They convince me of the income potential, so I quit my new job at the Broadmoor and work for the agency, mostly appealing to men with fetishes.

As a newcomer, I'm typically sent to client interactions along with another woman. It's common to wear a role-playing outfit such as a French maid, cheerleader, or nurse. The client is charged $180 per hour, and I only earn $80, but that's still good money.

Sometimes, the men only want me to chew gum and blow smoke in their face. One time, we meet a guy with a foot fetish, and he wants me to rub his feet while he pleasures himself. It is frequently disgusting and weird, and I don't know how to react, so I laugh it off. How crazy it is for some idiot to pay me for this? The work isn't difficult or gratifying.

Many times, I'm sent to the guy's home and he takes drugs while I'm there. I am glad to accompany my coworker, Claudia, so it seems safer, even though she's always drinking on the job. I'm too scared to drink before or during the *dates*.

I am constantly worried that something bad is going to happen. How would I know if the guy is a serial killer? So far, I've been lucky. I simply have to be agreeable and pay attention to them. I need to keep them happy because the only way to be assigned the next job is to be rated with a stellar review.

Only the girls with a five-star rating get new bookings. An excellent review means more jobs, more tips, and more referrals. But my *friend* Claudia convinces me that we could earn even more money if we go out on our own. I start placing a few ads on Craigslist and receive some interest and a few weeks later, we are independent. I'm my own start-up company, yeah!

Claudia and I part ways several months later after she passes out in my car and pees all over the seat. It's bad enough to put up with gross clients, but Claudia is causing more trouble than she's worth, so, I decide to work alone. Clients frequently ask for more than fetish participation. Most escorts don't limit themselves to simple fetish fantasies. I know there are higher dollars to make if I became a "full-service escort." The men will pay more, so with that simple logic, I dive in headfirst.

* * *

"I don't believe in the future."
- *Theresa, from the motion picture,*
Looking for Mr. Goodbar

2 YEARS LATER, SEPTEMBER 2007, AGE 26

My parents have no idea what I'm doing; I tell them I'm still working in the catering business. They know something is going on, but I don't let on as to what it is. They live several hours away, so it is easy to lie to them. They know I've fallen away from the church, and they stop pushing the issue. I no longer need Jesus since He let me get raped, so I decide to go work for *the other guy*.

I am living a double life. Leah knows what I am doing and warns me about the ways I could get caught. I am trying to act normal until I can't do it any longer. It's getting harder to figure out what is normal anymore.

Full service means anything and everything sexual. It also means more money, and I only cater to extraordinarily rich men. I'm the boss, and I make sure they pay! I'm booking more repeat customers who want the *girlfriend experience*. It means lots of sex for them and an obligation to waste more money on me.

I demand my side of the girlfriend experience. It starts with eating at fancy restaurants and morphs into long weekends out of town, staying at the fanciest hotels, and enjoying expensive enter-tainment in Las Vegas. I also expect the men to pay for my trendy clothing, designer shoes, and jewelry, spending money on me like there's no tomorrow. I order room service with fancy food and expensive wine and easily rack up over $1,000 of charges. They never complain.

I'm charging $500. That's not per day; it's per hour. I always treat myself to the day spa on my time off. I earn enough cash to easily pay for a boob job. I buy a new car, a convertible Mazda Miata. I'm cool. I use the most expensive make-up and always look hot. I'm a skinny girl and I am rockin' it! Sometimes, I even check into a fancy hotel by myself and order expensive room service, just to waste the money they pay me.

I'm making more money than what top female lawyers earn. It is surreal. As soon as the cash comes in, it is going out the door. I'll be honest with you: I'm not good at managing money. I doubt you're surprised, but as long as the money's flowing in, it doesn't matter.

My biggest concern is that I'll be hoodwinked by an under-cover cop and get caught. With my friend Leah working with law enforcement, my worst nightmare is being arrested and having her watch me do a perp walk. But it is a risk I'm willing to take, and I'll be frank with you, I'm looking for trouble. I don't care enough to alter my behavior.

If you're going to provide the girlfriend experience, it's best to rotate two or three sugar daddies. One of them was Marty Bilkestri. I've been with Marty for several months and genuinely like him. A little more than that, but I'm good at suppressing my feelings.

Marty isn't stingy. He lavishly spends money on me, typically a few thousand dollars, several times a week. He's about forty-seven years old, a little pudgy as many middle-aged men get, and is going bald.

He's a lawyer in town and drives a large Lexus. After being his girlfriend for a while, he brags that his real wealth came from his investments. He's earning more from those investments than his legal practice. He's smart and developed real estate in the Denver, Boulder, and Colorado Springs areas over the past twenty years. At the time, neither of us know that he's less than six months away from losing his shirt in the major recession of 2008.

Marty is planning something special and books me for two nights; it's going to be the first time we're meeting at his house. His wife and children are out of town, and he is excited to host his *girlfriend* at his home located in the expensive Kissing Camels neighborhood, complete with a view of the famous rock formations, Garden of the Gods. I'm oblivious to the irony. I never would have guessed that it'd be our last encounter.

Within five minutes of my arrival, my clothes are off, and he has sex with me on the kitchen table, right where he and his family ate dinner. I'm disgusted with his choice, but I don't care enough to protest. A few hours later, we are doing it again on the living room couch, presumably where he and his children watch family movies together or open presents around the Christmas tree.

The next day, we have an expensive lunch, and he treats me to an afternoon of massage therapy. Of course, we go out for a fancy dinner and eventually return to his house. He needs to pick up his family at the airport the next morning, so I know I'll be going home later that evening.

The night before, the only thing we did upstairs was sleep. My hair tends to shed, so I know that many long strands were left throughout the house, including the bedroom. Marty knows it too, but he's unconcerned.

This time, he tells me that we were going to have sex upstairs. He was referring to the bed he and his wife share. After he speaks those words, that's when time goes into slow motion.

He's leading, and I watch my hand touch the smooth oak-stained stairway rail, and it hits me that the real reason we're at his house instead of a charming hotel, isn't to save money. It isn't the thrill from the risk of potentially getting caught. No, we're at his house so he can express his *intense hatred for his wife*. My stomach churns.

I'm halfway to the second floor and on the wall, merely a foot from my eyes, I see pictures of him with his wife smiling, obviously from better days. There are also pictures of his kids when they were babies, others with them young and in elementary school, and some more recent, with his sons in high school. I am only a few years older than his kids. Doesn't he see a problem with that? Is this what he's teaching his sons?

The realization hits me hard. I'm at his house because he completely and deeply despises his wife and wants to desecrate the marital bed *with me*. I'm just a means to an end for him. My motivation is so I can rape him back, dehumanize him like I was treated years ago in Estes Park. But that's not how he sees it, and *that pisses me off*.

I don't want to see pictures of his wife nor do I want to know anything about her. I don't want to see happy memories on a family vacation. I don't want to get to know his kids or hear about what they're like. I don't care. I don't want to care.

I don't hate his wife, but I don't want to know about the rest of Marty's life, for that would personalize him! I want to keep our relationship transactional. I refuse to think of his life outside of our encounters. I don't want to hear about why he's disappointed with his wife and why she doesn't fulfill his sexual needs.

The money he spends on me doesn't mean anything. He's ordering a girl like a pizza. He must be bankrupting himself both financially and morally.

I've started to notice the looks we receive when we're in public and people must be wondering why a late forty-something man is with a young woman more than twenty years his junior. Why am I with this old ugly balding guy? No one would ever view him as a good-looking older gentleman. Where are my standards? Even more revolting, I wonder why I have feelings for this guy? I don't have an answer.

I'm horrified as it sinks in that people *know* he's my sugar daddy. I don't want to be seen in public like this anymore, including going out of town on his business trips. I understand that he's not happy with his wife, but what does that make me? I'm so naïve, thinking that I'm more than just his little slut.

He's never going to fully allow me into his world. I'm never going to meet his friends and host parties for the neighbors. I'm never going to be invited for Thanksgiving dinner to meet his mother. He isn't going to be my savior. I wish he'd find someone else, and then this thought jumps into my head: *What if I'm not the only one he's with?* I feel cheated on when I realize that he might be seeing others. Whatever allowed me to assume he'd only want to be with me?

These feelings are manifesting physically, and I worry I might retch. All these thoughts race through my mind by the time we get to the top of the stairs, and he grabs my hand to bring me into the bedroom.

I think about running. I'm so alone even though he is right in front of me. I want to escape and find a way out of there, but I know that I won't. *Why am I so weak?* So instead, I suppress my feelings and take it; I know what to do. I close my eyes and let it happen, and I can't wait until it's over so I can go home.

* * *

It's a slow fade when black and white have turned to gray
Thoughts invade, choices are made, a price will be paid
When you give yourself away
People never crumble in a day

"A Slow Fade" - Casting Crowns

2 HOURS LATER, 12:10 A.M.

I've been home for an hour and have no intention of going to sleep anytime soon. I'm physically tired and mentally exhausted and feeling a little depressed. I vow never to go back to his house again.

My apartment is quiet, and I briefly look at my beautiful kitchen. I have gorgeous Italian marble floors, a granite countertop, custom kitchen cabinets, and expensive cookware, but it doesn't make me happy. My place is in the most prestigious area of Colorado Springs, where all the successful professionals live. My income is more than my parents ever dreamed of.

My neighbors are young doctors, accountants, and tech entrepreneurs. I've spent many times chatting with the wealthy people in my building. I'm finally part of the "in" crowd. I love talking to them about running a successful startup. I'm like them: young, rich, ambitious, and willing to take risks. I've told them I own a human resource consulting firm, and I enjoy being part of their world, *but my part is all a lie.*

I hear the phone ring, and I recognize the number as Marty's. I let it continue to vibrate, and with each ring, the noise becomes torturously irritating. Why is he calling me? I scream at the phone, but it continues to move on the counter from the vibration. I feel myself getting worked up.

You didn't buy my private moments! He thinks he owns a piece of me, and I wonder if I'll ever get it back. He can have my body, but he can't have my mind! Doesn't he understand that? I'm not someone he can call anytime, just to talk. I don't want to be his confidant, and I don't want to be his friend.

I start crying and defiantly ignore the phone. When is the debt they owe me going to be paid in full? I look at the roll of cash in my purse. I yank open the freezer and throw a handful of bills in there. There's at least another $2,000 in my purse, and I growl at it, grab it with both hands, run to the bathroom, and stuff it down the toilet, getting my arms wet up to my elbows. I seriously consider sticking my head in the toilet to drown myself. It'd be easier if it just ended, but I can't make myself go through with it.

I'm repulsed by the wad of bills, and I have zero respect for it. He doesn't think that I have my own life. He has no right to my time off. He doesn't deserve to know what I do when I'm not working. He doesn't see me as an individual, and I say aloud, "I'm a real person!" But even I'm not convinced.

I don't know who I'm more disgusted with, him or myself. I've made him pay, but *when has he paid enough*? I struggle with that concept. I am so confused and continue crying and go to my bedroom and lie down, pounding the pillows. I'm lost in the details of my nothingness.

1 WEEK LATER

My phone vibrates, and I expect it to be Marty again. He's been trying to get a hold of me, but I refuse to answer his calls. I wish he'd stop. When I look at the phone, I gasp when I recognize the number calling. Now I wish it were Marty.

The number belongs to my father, and he's calling my business phone! I get a sick feeling in my gut; my secret is out.

I blacklisted a client who was a real jerk a few weeks ago and told some of the other girls I know in the business. He couldn't get any dates. He figured out my real name and threatened to tell my family. I assumed he was bluffing because he was angry, but it looks like he followed through.

Oh my God, my dad knows I've been living a double life! He'd much rather have me homeless and living under a bridge than doing what I'm doing. I go into the closet and I start bawling my eyes out. I am breaking down from the stark realization that I have lost my family.

THE NEXT DAY

"It's Gergun," the man says when I answered my phone.

"Yeah, I know your number. What's going on?" I ask.

"I've finished the editing, and it looks great," he tells me. Gergun is a guy in a swinger's group that I frequently work for. He made a video several days ago, and I dressed up as Lara Croft from the hit video game and movie. I'd never made a video before and didn't think much about it until he called. In fact, I don't watch pornography, so I was clueless as to what happens in a typical video. I'm so naive.

"Oh, that's good I guess," I comment, not seeing the relevance.

"I've sent it to some friends of mine in Los Angeles, and they want you to come work for them."

"What do you mean?"

"They want to make you a porn star," he states without emotion.

I need to disappear and desperately want to get out of Colorado. Moving to L.A. would solve that problem, so it's an easy decision. Yes, it's impulsive, but that's how I operate, and it never crosses my mind what could be in store for me in Los Angeles.

Three days later, my plane lands in the bright California sunshine, and out of the corner of my eye, I catch the devil smiling. I've sold my soul.

Just like a lost soul
caught up in the Hollywood scene
All the parties and the limousines
Such a good actress hiding all her pain
Trading her memories for fortune and fame
"Fallen Angel" - Poison

PART 4, 2 YEARS LATER, FEBRUARY 2009, AGE 28

The length of the line is shocking. I'm employed by a pornography producer, and we're holding an open house. We've set up a couple of trailers in the warehouse parking lot, and they have me working the registration and screening desk. I help the prospective talent with the paperwork before meeting the owners in the trailer for a "go-see." The owner is also the producer and sometimes director, who will perform further screening.

It's a beautiful sunny winter day in the San Fernando Valley. I didn't know what to expect, but new girls continue to show up. I'm feeling old; they look so young and have their whole life ahead of them, yet they're willing to enter the world of pornography. Some will never show up for a filming, but most will be lured in by the quick money and dreams of stardom.

Don't they know that it'll change their life forever? I've been here for two hours, and I've signed up eight girls. I'm leading the innocent lambs to slaughter. But most incredulous to me is that I've registered three girls brought by their moms. Here comes another pair.

"Hello, we're here to sign up my daughter, you know, for a movie," states Dolly, a short woman with dark hair who looks to be in her early forties. She's embarrassed and calls what we do "getting into the movies."

"I'm here to get you registered," I answer with a friendly smile and hand a form and clipboard to the daughter. She's also petite, with dark black hair with a small, studded nose ring. She's pretty, but not gorgeous. She could stand to lose a few pounds, but she'll do fine.

"How soon will she get paid?" the mom asks.

"It takes four to six weeks," I casually answer, and she seems unpleased with that.

"That long?"

"Yes, that's the norm."

"When can she start?" Dolly asks but is frustrated that the payment isn't sooner.

"Within a week or so," I answer, curious about why she's so anxious for her daughter to have sex with strangers.

"Our rent is due on the twentieth, so is there a way she can start before then?"

"I don't know," I answer honestly.

She nervously responds, "You see, the recession is killing me, and we owe several months of back rent, and we'll be evicted if we don't make a payment real soon," she tells me with desperation. She must assume that I possess influence or decision-making capabilities. That couldn't be farther from the truth.

"Well, I can let the producer know that you want to start soon, but it'll be up to him. The first thing we need is this form filled out. What's your name?" I ask.

"Ariel," the girl responds.

I look at the mother again and recognize the family resemblance.

"Okay, let's get your bunny ears," I state and she gives me a confused look, so I explain further, "I need two forms of identification."

She hands me a student card from Glendale Community College and a driver's license; I do the math and calculate that she's nineteen years old. She fills out the form with her basic contact information and gives it back to me.

"Let's go over a few questions before you talk to the producer," I say, and she nods.

"Where do you live?"

"Van Nuys," Dolly answers.

"I assume you're not a virgin?"

"Um, that's right," she replies with an anxious laugh.

"Have you had anal sex too?"

"Um, yeah a couple of times. It was no big deal," she says and her voice trails off, self-conscious to be answering these questions in front of her mother.

"Once you're in this business, you'll quickly forget about being embarrassed."

"Yeah, I suppose that's right," Ariel concedes.

"I also have to know what you are willing to do, or more specifically, what you're *not* willing to do?"

"What do you mean?" Dolly asks.

"It's very simple, the more types of sexual acts and situations that Ariel is willing to perform, the more content videos she'll be cast in, and of course, the more money that she'll make. You can be busy several times a week."

"You don't have to do *everything*," Dolly tells her daughter. I don't understand specifically what she means by that, but it's a little too late to be the protective mama bear since she's presented her daughter as a living sacrifice.

"Mom, it's okay. We need the money. We can't be evicted and live on the streets, so what's the difference if I do one thing or everything?" Ariel states with little emotion, appearing to be more interested in quieting her mother than the ramifications of her decision.

Every girl will eventually find her own line in the sand. Being in the business, I understand that it depends on how much of your soul you're willing to sell.

I continue, "If you're willing to do anything, you'll be put on what's called a *no-no* talent list."

"What's that?" Ariel asks.

"That means you don't say 'no' to anything. You could be doing boy-girl, girl-girl, threesomes, etcetera."

"I hadn't really thought about it," Ariel answers and then adds, "Whatever gets me working sooner."

"The no-no list will do that," I say and look at Dolly.

Ariel looks at her mother who appears dejected, knowing that Ariel's life will change forever. But Dolly has no idea that it will be worse than whatever she can imagine. But then, who am I to judge anyone? I don't think past the consequences of today.

Dolly is looking at me, searching my face to determine if I'm trustworthy, and Ariel quietly nods her head and says, "I won't say no."

I meet Dolly's eyes and tell her what she wants to hear, "I'll look after her." I look at Ariel and tell her, "I'll be your friend, don't worry. I'll take care of you."

"Okay," Ariel responds and asks, "Have you made videos, too?"

"Yes," I tell them and list some of the movie titles I've been in. I'm suddenly feeling ancient.

"What about STD testing?" she asks sheepishly.

"I'll be testing you as soon as your paperwork is complete, and you'll be tested regularly. You'll want to bring the results to show the other actors. We're professionals here, and we make sure that no one is spreading any diseases," I say with pride. With pride? Really Jessica? I can't believe I feel that way.

But I continue despite my false bravado, "And don't even think about going off your birth control, the last thing we want is one of our girls getting an abortion. That would be irresponsible."

Ariel looks at her mother and says, "I'll be fine. Hopefully, I won't have to do it for too long."

"You can stop whenever you want to," I tell her, but I know that's a lie. They don't last long, because of either the emotional trauma, a drug overdose, or suicide.

"What's this section about fees?" Ariel asks while flipping through the paperwork.

"That's what we call the *kill fee*. We charge you $350 if you are scheduled to do a scene and don't show up, or for any reason, you are unable to perform."

"That's a hefty fine and seems unfair," Dolly squawks.

"Time is money, and we can't have everyone waiting around for one person to show up. It's standard in this business. Besides, there's plenty of other girls who are set ready and can be called in at a moment's notice," I tell them.

"Yes, I understand," Ariel says, giving in, then sheepishly asks, "Do you think I'm good-looking enough?"

"Of course. We'll get you looking so sexy that you'll have every man's full attention. Before we film, I'll take you shopping. We'll get your hair and makeup done and maybe get you a couple of new outfits," I tell her and give her a friendly wink.

"I'd like that," Ariel answers, perking up with the idea of being treated like an actress. Little does she know that those expenses will be deducted from anything she earns.

"And if you're working as a regular, you're eventually going to have to live closer. We want you within five miles," I explain, which has the additional benefit of keeping her out of her mother's house. There's no need to have *Mommie Dearest* get in the way.

"That makes sense," she comments, and Dolly looks more at ease.

"Okay, I want you to take this paperwork, wait in line over there, and talk to Kincade, the producer," I tell her and point to a few folding chairs near the trailer. "If he approves, he'll give you the address of a party we're having at his house tonight, and you can meet everyone. How does that sound?"

"Okay, that sounds pretty cool," Ariel answers with some enthusiasm, and I realize that I've enticed another underage girl to a party that will include drugs, booze, and a house full of predators.

"One last thing. There's no dating outside the industry," I instruct her, and she looks puzzled. She'll learn soon enough. If she has a boyfriend, I doubt he'll want her after she turns pro.

She walks towards the trailer as if heading to the gates of Hell. I can't watch any longer, so I turn around quickly and ignore the image out of the corner of my eye of the devil smiling.

20 MINUTES LATER

I see Ariel enter the trailer and I know what's going to happen next. They tell her that she'll make top dollar for the next movie, that is, if she has the perfect body. They'll make her strip in front of everybody, which is three people, including the director, producer, and a makeup artist.

They'll shine bright lights on her body and begin to inspect every square inch of it. The examination isn't erotic, but instead, it will find every possible flaw. The makeup artist is the producer's girlfriend, a former porn actress who aged out of the business. She'll have a clipboard to write down each blemish, mole, skin irritation, and every bit of cellulite on Ariel's body. All the imperfections will be deducted from her "top dollar" rate.

The average person probably sees Ariel as an attractive girl, but as they verbally degrade her, they'll find over thirty-two distinct flaws, including some ridiculous things like her kneecaps looking wrinkled. They tell her that it makes her look forty years old, the kiss of death.

Ariel's ego will break like an eggshell, and she'll cry from the shallow physical criticism. Most nineteen-year-old teens have body image issues, so when you have multiple people publicly pointing out her faults with disapproving comments and making notes about them, she'll easily believe she's ugly and unworthy. They'll convince her that doing porn is the only way that someone will want her. They did this to me when I started, and I've never felt attractive since.

They also list non-physical imperfections. The director makes fun of her laugh, her personality, and when she mumbles her words, he calls her stupid and useless. It isn't long before she believes everything they're saying.

I try to convince myself that Ariel is different and can handle it, but I've seen too many get chewed up and spit out in this industry. It doesn't matter that she fully understands that the public will see her performing sex acts. She'll be coerced into far more extreme circumstances than she can imagine. I've seen girls lied to, told that the other actors will be gentle.

Girls are lied to about who will view the videos. Content is never limited to overseas distribution. They tell that to a lot of newbies; they say anything to get their clothes off. It's always posted online or used as blackmail for more content. They have no qualms about sending content to family, friends, and employers. Most of the time, the girls are devastated and their life is never the same.

8 HOURS LATER, 11:15 P.M.

Ariel is completely wasted, a goat among mountain lions, but I'm unable to help her. Besides, what can I do? She signed up for this, and if I say anything to dissuade her, the producer will have a fit, and I'll be out of a job and my reputation will evaporate. I'll never be able to get work again, and then what will I do? I don't have family that I can go back to.

Soon, my worst fears come true when the producer needs my help upstairs. So much for waiting for the STD test results. They escort Ariel to a bedroom with three guys in the room. She's stumbling around, obviously intoxicated, and the producer tells me that I may have to jump in and help.

I smile and tell him, "Whatever you want." He nods his head, pleased with my compliance.

Ariel is close to passing out and is unaware of what's about to happen. She offers to show the producer that she can star in a gangbang. She *will* be violated. But I know she's clueless about how bad it could go and for the next hour; the three men brutally rape her while the producer watches. I assist Ariel when asked, but she's the center of attention.

She passes out and has no idea what's happening. My job is to prop her up and verbally encourage the guys raping her. I'm eager on the outside and dying on the inside. Ariel must have lied about her experience with anal sex because one of the guys rips her open and there's blood everywhere. It's sickening to watch.

They finally finish and the producer instructs me to go clean up the bedsheets. He doesn't mention cleaning up Ariel. I'm left to mop up the mess that I've partially created. I gather some warm washcloths and clean the blood off her.

She regains consciousness, and her eyes communicate that she understands what I'm doing. I start to cry, realizing that merely a few hours ago, this girl was probably a typical teenager, trying to help her mom with financial troubles.

She was raped in front of me, and I let it happen, without a word spoken or a protest made. I don't know this girl at all, nor her history, but I feel a sympathetic connection. I wonder how she will react. If she needs the money, she'll continue putting up with the uncaring harshness of this business.

I hope I never have to see her mother again. I try to convince myself that I'm not responsible, but I can't stop the guilty feelings, especially since she doesn't know the downhill slide she's started. The producer will ask me to help train her body to be more receptive to anal sex.

"Thanks," she mumbles to me.

"Sure; I'm almost done cleaning you up. I'm sorry that I didn't do anything to help you," I say, but can't think of any valid excuse to give her. Her response stuns me.

"What's there to apologize for? I've seen enough porn to know this would happen. I'm a little surprised that it happened so soon, but I guess I better get used to it," she says with a nervous laugh. She's correct, and I'm lost for words, and it's one of my saddest moments in Los Angeles.

I grasp that it didn't matter who was at the registration table, and Ariel would've been in the same situation, yet I feel responsible since I signed her up. I'm the one who told her mother that I'd take care of her. I've done a lousy job and Ariel will eventually resent us both.

* * *

And the years rolled slowly past
And I found myself alone
Surrounded by strangers I thought were my friends
I found myself further and further from my home
And I guess I lost my way
"Against the Wind" - Bob Seger and
the Silver Bullet Band

THREE DAYS LATER

"What's wrong with you?" Mike the director is asking me. He's annoyed that I've thrown up on set, so now we need to stop and wipe it up.

One of the cameramen throws me a towel and says, "Clean your mess!" and everyone laughs at me. We are doing a parody of the *Jersey Shore* television program.

More often, when I'm in front of a camera, I feel slimy and polluted. Feminists keep telling me that taking charge of my sex is empowering, and sex work is the same as any other career. But this business is breaking me, not empowering me. I can't imagine that anyone in this business believes they're in charge of their life.

I mop up as quickly as possible. I live in L.A. with millions of people, yet I'm isolated and alone. It's not just me; it's all the actors. Civilians don't understand. In this industry, the term 'civilian' means anyone who is not part of the porn industry.

We're a relatively small group of *actors* who look down on the amateurs ruining pornography. We tend to only hang out with other *actors.* It's difficult to interact with anybody outside of the industry; they don't understand our world. That reinforces the 'us and them' mindset.

When it comes to dating, it's common to date another actor within the business. I've had a few boyfriends in the industry while I've lived here. Why would a normal civilian date a pornstar? It's an unwritten rule that we porn stars can't date a civilian. When I'm in a relationship, it's acceptable to have sex with somebody else if it's for a content video. That's a professional setting. However, it would be considered cheating if I have sex with anyone else off camera.

I've been told many times, 'Who will want you?' and 'Who else will book you?' Us actors are easily replaced and if I earn a reputation of being difficult, no one will hire me. I believe that this work is my only lifeline.

I can't even cling to the fantasy of someday switching to real Hollywood acting. That's never going to happen, and even *my* impetuous brain knows that. I'm left with the only choice: perform. If I mess up any scene, I'll be blackballed.

I've lost my family and friends, so there's no one to help me. I haven't talked to my parents in a long time. I've also lost Leah as a friend because she can't understand what I'm doing, and the last time I talked to her, she told me that she doesn't recognize me. I've been pretending to be someone else for so long that I forgot how to be me. I can't separate my screen character from my real life.

Because of my mistake, the director has decided to take a five-minute break. One of the guys was having performance issues, and I see him go to his jacket, grab something, and head to the bathroom. We all know what he's going to do. This twenty-four-year-old has a syringe and will directly inject his penis with an enhancement drug. He returns very ready.

The director decides to change up the script. I'm being punished. The men slap me around on camera. Do you want to guess how I react? As I've been taught, I ask for harsher treatment, and my performance will easily convince the viewer that I'm enjoying their sadistic behavior.

I must deserve it. I didn't anticipate how violent and destructive this business is on my body. And I also wonder, what kind of person likes to watch this crap? I'm about to cry, but I concentrate to suppress the feelings. There will be time to cry later. The director nods at me in approval, and I'm so broken that I eat up his morsel of positive reinforcement.

2 HOURS LATER

Luckily, there is a shower on-site, and I use the soap lavishly to clean up. But there isn't enough soap in the world to wash away the filth. The Palmolive I used a lifetime ago won't make me clean either. I've no idea where my life is going after losing contact with my family. Pornography is all that I know. I wanted to show God that I could find the bottom of the sin barrel, and I certainly achieved that goal.

As I'm leaving, I pass the door to the editing room, which is slightly ajar, and I'm surprised to hear my voice. I peer into the room and notice the producer's son is editing my performance in the content video from a few hours ago.

The editor is ten years old. I know his age because they had a birthday party for him a couple of weeks ago. Parenting books never recommend a birthday party with a bunch of porn stars. Now, this ten-year-old is editing my movie. At what age did he start watching porn? At what age did pornography become normal to this kid?

He notices me standing there and then casually observes without making eye contact, "You really liked getting slapped around and fucked by those guys." He's unemotional and completely sincere.

I'm dumbfounded by his crassness and nonchalant attitude. I want to tell him that pornography is ruining our culture, of young people's view of sex and how to treat women. I'm about to lecture him, but then I realize, *this kid's already lost.* Besides, if I say anything negative about the industry and he tells someone, I'll be the one to suffer. I open my mouth and start to say *something*, but no words come out.

He goes back to editing the video, and after a few more seconds, he turns to me and says, "I like your work, I'm a big fan."

I'm even more flabbergasted and at a loss for words after his compliment. The last thing I want is to have fans, people who glorify my lifestyle. It's bad enough when an adult tells me they're a fan, but what am I supposed to say when an admirer of *my work* has yet to start puberty?

SEPTEMBER 2010, AGE 29

I'm a Colorado girl who grew up in a small town, thinking Denver was a big city. Los Angeles is full of people, famous landmarks, and large buildings, but it's nothing compared to seeing the Manhattan skyline from forty stories high. It's not the tallest residential building in New York, but I'm awestruck, nonetheless.

It almost looks fake. It's so grand, like a scene out of a movie. I can't believe that I'm in a Manhattan penthouse overlooking Central Park with seven other girls. Each of us porn girls will earn $1,600 an hour for the next four hours. This is great money for me because the older I get, the lower my rate will go.

He has a two-floor unit, and the people in Central Park look far away. I'm overwhelmed by the massive wall of windows and this apartment screams, "I'm super-rich." To supplement my income, I've offered high-end escort services and this guy flew all of us out, first-class to New York City.

A limousine picks us up, and we arrive at his place at about 9:00 p.m. We start with champagne in the limo, and there's more for us at his gorgeous built-in bar. It tastes fine, and I assume it's high-end like the rest of the residence. I step closer to the glass windows and barely detect the vibration and noise from the city below.

Mr. Carey Vleason is older with a full head of gray hair, at least sixty years old, but I'm not sure how he'll handle eight of the finest sex machine porn workers from Los Angeles. I suddenly worry that he'll have a heart attack. But we get paid first from his hidden safe as he doles out $7,000 per person, which includes a $600 tip.

I accept a glass of champagne and soak in the exquisiteness of his home. I see several paintings on the wall, and I'm confident each one costs a fortune. But abstract art isn't my style, so I'm not impressed with pictures that look like a child's finger painting.

There is a large living room with a bar area that can seat at least twenty people, and this guy lives alone. So, why does he need room for dozens?

The furnishings are modern and uninviting, a place where I'm afraid to touch anything for fear of breaking it. The decorations look fragile, and the impersonal sterile, and phony style fits the stereotype of a Manhattan socialite. I've gone from serving rich people at the Stanley Hotel to serving the rich in other ways.

At the far end of the room, I notice three steps up to a large platform, and the beautiful grand piano catches my eye. The dark mahogany instrument is perfectly polished, and I'm drawn to it. I press a few of the keys, and it sounds noticeably better than the cheap church pianos I remember from a lifetime ago. It's without a speck of dust, and I wonder if he plays or whether it's just for show.

I press a few more keys, and the strong, crisp, and beautiful notes bring me alive, and I'm lost in my own world for a moment. The next thing I know, Carey is standing behind me. I turn around embarrassed, realizing that I shouldn't be touching his expensive things. He didn't hire me to admire his pristine $100,000 Steinway.

"Do you play?" Carey asks.

"Yes, but it's been a while. I hope you don't mind that I'm admiring this piano. It's beautiful," I sincerely profess. I had a decade's worth of classical piano lessons growing up, but it was on a junky old church upright piano.

"I don't mind at all," Carey tells me and smiles. Is he proud that he's impressed a porn star? "Everything here is quite expensive, including the piano, but it all can be replaced. It's the time spent with people that's priceless. Once the moment is gone, it's gone forever."

"Yes, of course," I reply, thinking that he is referring to his sexual expectation for the evening. Including the travel costs, he spends over $75,000 for the *time spent with people*. But that's not what he meant.

"I love music. I get lost in the sonata when it's playing, and try to get absorbed in the moment," Carey tells me.

"Yes, that's lovely." I nod, and I'm surprised at how genuine Carey is.

He continues, "I feel the music and want it to tell me something, and mean something to me, make an emotional connection with me. But when the moment's over . . ." he trails off in silence.

"I understand."

"I don't know how to play. I've had many people entertain me on the Steinway. I enjoy those moments when I have the opportunity. Will you play something?"

"Sure," I agree. But then I feel nervous, knowing that Carey is used to professional musicians playing beautiful renditions of Beethoven and Mozart. What's he going to think of a porn star who hasn't played the piano in over a decade?

I sit down on the bench, turn, and look at him. He nods at me with approval and an encouraging look, so I figure I'll give it a try. After all, playing the piano is not what he hired me for, but if that's what he wants, I'll play.

I play a song that I learned as a teenager, a simple song with a nice melody, and once I start concentrating, it comes back to me. I notice Carey return to the couch with a few of the other girls.

I hear them laughing and chatting like they would at a regular party. Nothing sexual is happening, so I focus on playing the song. A few minutes later, he notices when I briefly stop playing. He waves to me, indicating that he wants me to continue, so I do.

When I finish the song, I play another, and the next thing I know, I've played for over two hours. I look back over to the couch and see Carey all alone. He has on all his clothes except for his shoes.

The other girls are standing around the bar, drinking and chatting. I decide to stop playing and join them. I check my purse and notice my white scarf. I usually bring a scarf that's been washed with lots of bleach. I smell the scarf and the pungent smell invokes a clean feeling and then I ask, "Did you all sneak into the bedroom with him and I didn't notice?"

"Oh no!" one of the girls remarked and explained, "We were talking to him, and he asked me to rub his feet, so I assumed he had a foot fetish. But nothing happened. He was lying on his back and I was working his feet while Billie cradled his head in her lap and rubbed his temples. And then you'll never guess what happened next."

"What?"

"He fell asleep, and he hasn't moved since."

"Are you sure he's still alive?" a different girl teased. But having a dead client is no joking matter, so I walk over to him and confirm he's breathing.

"Is he drunk or doped up?"

"He doesn't seem to be," Billie added.

Reality hits me. He had no intention of having sex with any of us tonight. He simply wanted to be surrounded by pretty girls. He's a sad and lonely old man who probably has lots of phony friends, but no one to truly love. His circumstances depress me, but then who am I to criticize?

What friends do I have? Why would someone love the real me when I'm pretending so often? My so-called friends and lovers are just strangers. We're all fake, and we know that there's a certain amount of time left in this business and once we're used and washed up, we'll end up being just as sad and lonely as Carey, but without the money. He hired us to fill the silence.

JUNE 2011, AGE 30

There's an online tracker that captures our STD test status, and the producers and directors have access to it. I haven't seen Ariel's update in a while. In our industry, people usually know when someone has voluntarily left the business. But I get a sinking feeling in the pit of my stomach, knowing the other reasons when someone doesn't get tested. It usually means they've either overdosed or killed themselves. I've tried to contact her, but without success.

I'm now thirty years old and aging out of the business. The producer wants me to do softcore pornography. While that sounds easier and less degrading than what I've been doing, his reason is insidious. He wants to bring in the casual female viewer. I know from my experience that men want to see the act, but women want to know why they're doing the act.

Softcore pornography is sneaky because it's luring in the female and cautious viewer. It's social engineering, and that's exactly what it's meant to do, to get people used to pornography and remove any shame or uneasiness. Normalizing it so they become more sexualized so the hardcore stuff won't seem so shocking.

The tightness in my stomach is even more pronounced because I remember when Ariel first started. She was an innocent kid with her whole life ahead of her, standing in line, lured by *easy* money so her mom can pay the rent. That was years ago.

I was remembering that I promised her mom I'd take care of her and be her friend, but I never did. I failed them both, caught up in my own misery. I want to apologize to Ariel and tell her to get out while she still can. I want to tell her how miserable I am and how much I regret the choices I've made and that it isn't too late for her. I want to tell her my story the next time I see her, but I can't find her.

What's happened to her now? I have no idea, and honestly, I am afraid to find out. I now realize that I'm part of the problem. She was barely nineteen when she started, just a kid. Her view of sex is completely reprogrammed. But it's not just her.

I'm in the business of sexualizing children. I know that more and more children are viewing pornography at an earlier age. That's the trend, and I doubt it's going to turn around anytime soon. I've seen girls get raped, and I've been coerced and threatened many times myself. And yet they try to sell it to the public that women like to be treated like that. But it's all a bunch of crap.

I've been cheerleading for the wrong team. Ariel isn't the only girl I've recruited into this industry. The weight of my actions overwhelms me when I say it again aloud, "I'm the problem." I'm going insane, and I bury my head in my hands and cry.

Horny guys flippantly ask me how they can get into the porn industry, but I ask them, how can I get out? The men sell their souls too, but the outside world never hears about it.

I've suppressed the truth, convincing myself that it's just entertainment for adults. That it helps empower women, or spices up a couple's sex life, but it's a lie. It's the younger viewers I worry about most. It's so easy to access porn sites, and many of the companies have website names similar to legitimate sites for children.

How do these young teen brains view relationships after watching pornography? How do their minds change after watching brutal and violent pornography? How do these young boys treat girls? Do the girls expect to be treated badly? Do they see that as *normal?* I'm afraid of the answers. I twisted these young minds, and I can't stand to look at myself.

Pornography isn't real life, and it's seeping into young people and it changes them, obliterating their view of what a loving, healthy relationship looks like. Where is the love? There isn't any. We're teaching society that sex is merely a means for instant gratification and there's no need for family or relationships. We're destroying the beauty of deep and meaningful connections. And damn it, I've been part of selling that lie.

I scream out loud. But I finally know deep in my heart that I can't do it anymore, and a temporary sense of peace fills me because I now have the strength and resolve to leave the city of fallen angels.

PART 5, JULY 2011, AGE 30

"You're running girls?" I ask incredulously.

"Yeah, I've been doing it at the Denver Tech Center for over a year now," Sammie replies.

"How's that going?" I ask with great fascination.

"Really well, and it provides me a six-figure salary," my friend answers. I'd known Sammie O'Fesslinger back in Los Angeles, and we bonded because we're both Colorado girls. She was signed with a different pornographer, although we worked on a couple of content videos together. I respect her because she kept herself (mostly) away from drugs and alcohol. I know she left the business about a year ago and moved back to Denver.

I was unsure about where to find work. Working again as a youth pastor was laughable, so I considered service jobs such as a waitress or barista to bring in a little money until I figured out my next move. I haven't enjoyed the drastic income reduction. No more limousines and fancy lifestyles for me.

Soon after I leave California, we meet for lunch as I am curious about what she's been doing since leaving the life. I want to see what kind of work she's doing and how she fills out her resume for the time spent in Los Angeles.

But the notion of waitressing, even at a nice steak house like *Elway's*, is quickly dispelled because I'm genuinely impressed with Sammie, and my respect for her skyrockets. I suddenly view her as a success story of someone getting out of pornography, creating a life, and starting her own business. It's an easy route to large dollars and I can skip the struggle. I don't consider any of the pitfalls, so my attention is focused on this new curiosity.

"So, how many girls are working for you?" I ask earnestly.

"I've got four."

"Are you working too?" I inquire.

"Only if I feel like it. I organize everything from setting up the online profiles, coordinating appointments, and paying the girls, but I'm hooking up with only a few select clients."

"Yes, that's much better," I laugh, for I completely understand the appeal.

"Some of the pro ballplayers are clients, and they pay extra for being discreet, so it's very lucrative," Sammie explains.

"Oh, nice," I agree and nod my head in approval and comment, "It's great to be out of porn, isn't it?"

"Yeah. Speaking of L.A., I assume you heard about Ariel, right?"

"What are you talking about?" I ask and immediately become concerned.

"It happened right around the time you were coming back to Colorado. Overdose."

"No!" I gasp and place my hand over my mouth. This is horrible news, and my prior guilt floods back.

"They found her in a crappy motel room."

"I was afraid she might be using," I comment. What a shame.

"That girl had serious issues, so I'm not surprised," Sammie scoffs.

"She's just a kid," I defend her. "They really messed her up."

"I suppose," Sammie replies and shrugs her shoulders as if to say that Ariel wasn't the first and wouldn't be the last. Unfortunately, I know she's right, but that doesn't prevent me from simultaneously experiencing a wide range of emotions, from anger to sadness to guilt.

FEBRUARY 2012, AGE 31

I decide to do it the *right* way. I didn't have that much money when I left Los Angeles, but enough to make a deposit on a four-bedroom apartment in Denver, and I decide to do what Sammie does, only better. I'm an entrepreneur again, and I'm so excited.

Sex always sells, and there's no shortage of guys looking for a hookup. There are plenty of girls willing to do this, so I provide a safe place for everyone. I protect my girls and take care of them. I convince myself that this will make up for not taking care of Ariel. This is a better way to be in the sex business.

I meet several talented photographers and set up a Facebook account, which helps me in two ways. First, the photographers post pictures of hot girls and tag them, the makeup artists, hairstylists, and anyone else associated with making the girl look attractive. I Facebook friend all of them and use them as a pool for recruiting.

Second, I use Facebook to screen the customers. I check out the guy's Facebook account to see if he looks normal. I reject any man that has any weird or unusual posts. This method has so far worked well for me.

I convince a few girls to try it out a few nights a week, and they quickly earn more money working for me part-time than working a civilian job full time. Some of these young chicks can retire by the time they're my age, and I encourage them to save their money, but they aren't listening to me. Believe me, I understand.

I'm a businesswoman, and I'm ready for success. It's an ego boost living in a high-end apartment with other professional people. I want to meet them all. Without me doing the actual sex work, I bet within six months I'll be dating and engaged to a doctor.

1 YEAR LATER, FEBRUARY 2013, AGE 32

"No one smacks my property!" I scream at the man. The last thing I need is some idiot bruising one of my girls and arguing about it in my living room where a potential customer might be waiting. He looked like he was about to leave, but I won't let him.

"What happened?" I demand.

"Nothing, I made a mistake," Misty answers first.

"I don't know what her problem is. We agreed about what was going to happen, so it shouldn't be a surprise when it does!" counters Joe Kowgilt, one of my regulars.

"You don't get to smack her around if there's a problem. You've been coming here often enough to know that, right?"

"I suppose," he answers with sarcastic indifference; that only sets me afire.

"I don't care what agreement you had. If there's a problem with one of my girls, you come to me. You don't hit her or anyone else. This is not a sex simulation video game. If you leave a mark on my property, I'm going to cut off your balls," I growl at him and the look in my eyes portrays that I am dead serious.

With my tall height, I am eye to eye with this guy and have no intention of backing down. This is a regular customer who's never been violent, so I need to flash enough anger to make sure that it doesn't happen again.

"Okay, I get it," he responds. "I should know better," Joe says to Misty directly.

I don't see swelling or bruising on Misty, so there isn't any damage. I also want Joe to save face, so I turn my disdain towards Misty. "If you agreed, why is there a problem?" I angrily ask her, my eyes bugging out.

"I don't know. Maybe I just wasn't ready. It was the first time anyone asked me to do *that,*" she states and exhales loudly.

"Well, you need to get it together," I scold her and she nods in compliance. My need to dominate lessens, so I make a suggestion. "Let's get you two a drink and take a moment to calm down, okay? Then maybe you could start over?" I ask Joe with encouragement and an easy relaxed smile.

"That works for me," Joe states and looks at Misty, "Can we push the *reset* button?" he suggests.

Good, the crisis is averted, and I look at Misty, who replies, looking more relaxed, "Sure."

"Will Maker's Mark whisky suit you?" I ask and head to the bar; I already know his answer.

"Yes ma'am," Joe answers and follows me. I'm pleased that I won't lose this transaction because these two idiots can't communicate.

A FEW HOURS LATER

It's almost midnight and the last customer leaves on a busy Wednesday evening. My remaining employee is Reese, a short skinny girl, cute and innocent-looking with long reddish-blonde hair. She is one of those women who'll get carded at bars for the next fifteen years because she doesn't look fully developed and mature even though she's twenty-one.

Reese is a part-time spin class instructor at the local gym and doesn't have any body fat and weighs about ninety pounds. Since cycling is so popular in Colorado, her classes are always booked. I was in her spin class a few months ago and recruited her to work for me.

"Do you want a drink?" I ask her.

"Sure," she responds, and I pour us both a glass of Merlot and we relax in my living room.

"That was a busy evening for you; four guys make the time go fast," I comment and continue, "Were you in control of the situation?"

"Absolutely. I follow your instructions perfectly," she comments. When the girls stick to my procedures, everything runs smoothly. The guy is satisfied and no time is wasted.

"I might do this full-time," she throws at me.

"Really, I thought you wanted to become an insurance agent?"

"Yeah, I'd earn more if I quit my job at the gym and converted to full-time and pursued my license. But I'll never bank the amount of money I could get here," Reese answers, stating the obvious.

It will be a financial windfall for me if Reese works full-time, but I'm taken aback by her casual decision process. I have mixed feelings, leaning strongly against it. I can't discern why I react with inner conflict.

"You can't return to normalcy if you completely leave civilian life and come into this world," I point out.

8 MONTHS LATER, OCTOBER 2013, AGE 32

Reese turns out to be a great employee, working full-time and easily developing an established list of clients, and is keeping remarkably busy. Even better, she does everything I say and when I say it.

I have a great idea for her, so I head to the nearest Target store for new clothes. I will update her profile and send out an announcement to all my clients this afternoon.

I go to Target to purchase several items in the *Hello Kitty* line of clothing. I notice that it's located in the girl's department, and I buy everything they have, including pajamas, shorts, underwear, tops, training bra, earrings, and a purse. I don't care what it costs since I'll be deducting the amount from what I pay her. I'm excited to dress up Reese in the outfit and put together a photo collection.

While shopping, one part of me dreaded that it would bring out the worst in the men. Another part of me saw it as a social experiment. I know men like fresh young-looking girls in porn, but I didn't want to believe they would act out their fantasies with Reese.

I return to the apartment, and Reese is ready. She tries on the clothes in several different combinations and fixes her hair in different styles. I take tons of pictures of her in a variety of poses.

The one I like the most is a sexy picture of her lying face down on the bed reading a *Cosmopolitan* magazine while wearing the *Hello Kitty* underwear and bra, nicely showing off her rear end. I also like the frontal view of the same pose that displays her small amount of cleavage.

It's super cute, so I update her profile and advertise that tonight will be Reese's *Hello Kitty* theme night and encourage the guys to *come and get it while it's hot!* I also post that there are no reservations tonight because she's on a first-come, first-serve basis, starting at 6:00 p.m.

I pat myself on the back for being a marketing genius. I know they're attracted to the novelty of being the first one that no one else has had. On the website, I instruct the men to park and wait in their car so I can give them a raffle ticket and the lucky winner will have first dibs on Reese.

I'm publicizing the evening like I'm selling concert tickets to the most popular act in town, and I can't wait to find out if I'm as smart as I think I am. It will turn out to be a night I won't ever forget.

My apartment balcony overlooks the parking lot. So, at around 5:45 p.m., I casually look outside, and you won't believe what I saw.

There are at least ten guys waiting in their vehicles. I recognize many as repeat customers but I also see several unfamiliar faces, and I can tell, they're looking for Reese. I'm confident they're here for her because I'm too familiar with the sexually frustrated look in their eyes. Then it becomes eerie.

It hits me like a ton of bricks, and it's a powerful emotion that I've never experienced before. I left Los Angeles because I irrevocably recognized that it's a toxic and exploitive industry. But pornography is merely a piece of a larger problem.

The men in the parking lot are a clear message to me: those addicted to pornography and escort girls don't want women, *they want children*. I feel as if a dark cloud comes over my head and the air around me feels cold and sinister.

They're attracted to innocence, and it's a turn-on for them to *destroy that innocence*. I posted pictures of Reese who is twenty-one years old but is dressed up in a *Hello Kitty* outfit to make her look like she's twelve. I threw raw meat up in the air, and a bunch of junkyard dogs are waiting to *devour her*. It's a scene of pure evil, and I unmistakably see the devil smiling.

It's 6:00 pm, and my phone is blowing up with text messages. They all want her. I'm staring at these guys from the balcony, and they start to whistle at me, trying to get my attention. It's a scene from Hell, and they want to be the first to corrupt and violate the *Hello Kitty* girl. My breathing becomes erratic, and I start to sweat. I've literally created monsters, and now I'm scared out of my mind.

But it's not the evil that these guys want to perpetuate that hurts me most; it's the fact that *I set this up*. I created this. I'm the one enabling *evil*, and I start to cry with the tears blurring my vision.

I am a predator too. I've referred to my employees as *my property*. I foolishly believed that if I were the one running the business I could protect them, but I did the opposite. I exploited them. I am no better than the pimp on the street. I'm not a successful businesswoman, so no wonder I can't attract a doctor or accountant to marry. I'm a monster too.

I can't take it anymore, and I scream at myself and walk back into the apartment. Reese rushes towards me in a panic, for it must have sounded like I was being murdered. I tell her to go home, and she's confused, wondering why her *event* is being canceled at the last moment.

"Don't you get it? Don't you understand that those men are disgusting animals out there?" I ask her.

"Huh? Didn't you make the announcement about this? Didn't you want a large turnout?" she asks, still confused as to what the problem is.

"Yes, I'm sorry that I almost allowed this to happen to you."

"Isn't that what you hired me for?"

"You should go home. You need to get out of this life," I implore her.

"What? You've lost your mind," she shakes her head and leaves.

"Wait!" I scream down the hallway but she doesn't turn around. I can't prevent her from surrendering herself to the wolves.

I'm sickened when I fully understand what motivates these guys. My eyes are finally seeing it all. It's the fantasy of defiling the innocent child that brought them to the parking lot. There's nothing more revolting than someone who wants to have sex with a child. *What. Have. I. Done?*

I pass by a mirror in my apartment, and I stare at myself. I don't like what I see, and I hate what I've become. This is the moment I hit rock bottom and I can no longer live this corrupt life.

My head is hurting and my smearing makeup gives me a ghoulish countenance. I want to throw up, and my knees are wobbly, like I'm going to melt into the floor like the Wicked Witch of the West. When I left Hollywood, I tried to rebuild my life without God, but that doesn't work!

It is time to shut all of this down and I whisper aloud, "God, my sins put you on the cross, can you ever forgive me? I need you now more than ever. I know I've spent the last decade railing against you, but I need your light and I need your strength. Please save me, I am nothing without you."

I stare at my phone, still in my hand, and see hundreds of names that profit from me like I have profited from them. My contact list doesn't include one real friend or someone who loves me. This life has given me everything except friends; it's been extraordinarily unfulfilling. I throw the phone across the room and it breaks into several pieces.

* * *

"The light shines in the darkness, and the darkness has not overcome it."

- John 1:5

PART 6, SIX DAYS LATER, NOVEMBER 2013

The last couple of days were crazy. I needed help to shut down my brothel and decided to contact an old friend, Pastor Dan. I attended some of his sermons when I was nineteen, a lifetime ago, and hoped he would remember me. I was upset and drunk when I called him and told him I was ready to surrender, but now I am scared to do that.

For the next several days, he called me and left several voice-mails, but I was reluctant to call him back. On the third day, I finally answer his call.

"Jessica, I've been trying to reach you for days. I want to help you," Pastor Dan tells me.

"You can't help me!" I blurt back at him. I've been feeling demonic the past few days, and my mind won't stop whirling.

"I'll help you," he implores and quickly adds, "I know you're in trouble and it's all hands on deck. You have my undivided attention," he tells me. I believe him, so I tell him what I've been doing for the past decade.

"I'm so broken," I admit to him, crying into my phone.

"You're not alone and you can trust me."

"But I deserve God's judgment and that means enduring His wrath!" I cry out and continue, "I'll get what I deserve. What if I leave my life of sin only to receive immediate payback? What if I fall in love and marry a man that's a closet child molester?" I ask, expressing one of my greatest fears.

"Our God is a loving and forgiving God," he says with calm and reassurance. "You know that broken people attract other broken people. You must stop the cycle. If you surrender to God, you'll have a clean slate. Only then can you choose to heal."

I pause a moment to let his words sink in. It must have been divine intervention, because my heart told me I had Christ's full attention, and I simply needed to move towards Him. "Okay, here's my address," I whisper.

THE NEXT DAY

He's a good-looking man at six feet, four inches tall and is physically imposing. But he's the opposite of intimidating; he's a kind and gentle man with an easy-going demeanor. Pastor Dan's presence immediately brings calm to my situation.

This truly is the end of an era for me and the start of a new path. I want to begin the healing process, but I'm anxious about several things. One of them is being investigated by law enforcement. He helped me dispose of my electronic devices and any trace of illegal activity. I've gone mostly undetected by the authorities, and I want that to continue, so we purge any evidence we could find.

While loading boxes in my car, Pastor Dan discovered a bunch of pornography DVDs and sex toys in the trunk. I'm holding on to them in case I fail out of the program and need something to fall back on. Pastor Dan isn't buying any of that.

He said the first part of the recovery process was to throw all that stuff away. So, I've come full circle from when I threw my Christian books into the dumpster in Estes Park to trashing the evidence of my sinful life.

I've been living a double life for so long; I'm worried I won't be able to find the real me. What if I find the real me and I don't like what I see? Or even worse, what if I can't change? Another doubt is creeping into my head, whispering in my ear that it won't work and I'll fall back *into the life.*

I'm done fighting God, and I know how wrong it was and that's how I lost myself. But I'll be honest with you; I'm a little nervous. In two more days, I'll be going to Kentucky to stay at the Refuge for Women. It's a faith-based organization that provides housing, counseling, healing, and training for women who have escaped sexual exploitation. It's a new organization, and it had an opening for me, so I'll be driving to Kentucky.

But I have seen some church organizations that are ill-equipped to save a girl like me. I have doubts because I personally haven't seen them succeed, but then realize that those who did succeed wouldn't have been part of my past life. But now I'm ready to find the real me. The *me* that I would have been if none of this stuff ever happened.

I'm anxious because my future is unclear, and I don't know if this place will be able to help me. But there is one thing I am certain of, and it's a relief. I'm ready to surrender.

* * *

"To one who has faith, no explanation is necessary. To one without faith, no explanation is possible."

- *St. Thomas Aquinas included in* Summa Theologica

3 WEEKS LATER

My life is filled with structure and discipline, a noticeable change from before. The orderly way I'm living is an integral part of the Refuge for Women healing process. For the first time in my life, my sole purpose is to wake up and heal.

In the morning, I'm shocked by what's staring back at me in the mirror. I'm no longer a slave to my reflection, trying to look beautiful so someone will love me. In the past three weeks, I've gained thirty pounds, cut my hair, and stopped using makeup. I'm purposefully looking unattractive to see if the people at this recovery home will love and accept me.

They've organized my life down to the basics. In my space, I'm allocated ten hangers, four pairs of shoes, a bed, and a small dresser. Everything is simplified, and they teach us to be stewards of our own life.

But before I can manage the complicated stuff, I first need to master the fundamentals. Can I be on time for breakfast? Can I participate during the individual or group therapy sessions? Can I keep my space tidy? Can I get along with others?

Managing the little things is the building block to moving up to working through the larger parts of life. I've been taught to embrace the routine and focus on learning new positive habits. Each day, I have choices. For example, I decide whether to get myself out of bed each morning. I must choose to trust and be honest with the counselors. These choices will determine my future.

It's up to me to put in the time and effort to continue the healing process. To recover, I must do more than participate; I'm the one who must walk the recovery path, and repeat the same actions the next day.

Most importantly, I've put my trust in God. Faith is a big part of the program here, and I don't simply need God, *I embrace Him.* Later in the program, they will assist with life skills training, goal setting, financial planning, and assistance to eventually help me find a job. They will work with me to write up a multi-year life plan. But first, the emphasis is on getting the basics figured out.

I'm finding myself at peace and ready to recover my wounded soul. It won't be easy to work through the trauma of the last decade, but it feels good to have taken the first steps.

2 WEEKS LATER

I've been diagnosed with adult ADHD, which is attention deficit hyperactivity disorder. I've probably had this since childhood, and it continued into adulthood, affecting many parts of my life. For the first time, my behavior and life choices make sense.

People with ADHD typically display behavior such as impulsiveness, problems focusing on a task, poor planning, being easily distracted, making careless mistakes, taking unnecessary risks, and someone who has a tough time resisting temptation. It also can include behavior problems such as not following through and not realizing the consequences of decisions. When I heard that from the counselor, she was summing up my entire life. I'm also stressed and sometimes depressed.

This diagnosis doesn't let me off the hook or make excuses. I own the decisions I've made, but it helps explain how I'm programmed and why some of the events in my life came about. Clearly, I have some work to do, but I'm grateful to have this basis of understanding. Now my goal will be to build the strength and willpower to overcome these unhealthy habits, or at least temper them down.

Everyone else in this recovery home has been traumatized, some worse than me, from years of being sex trafficked. All of us have problems and issues to work through. As bad as this sounds, I take some comfort that I'm not the only messed-up person in this world. They all tell me that their sex buyers regularly watched pornography, and I now understand the strong connection to trafficking. I apologize to them for my role in porn.

The personality dynamics have been fascinating to observe. It's like we are all trying to determine what boundaries we can push and if anyone in the recovery home is there to break you. We've all been broken down by someone in our past, whether it's a pimp or porn director, and we all keep waiting for the other shoe to drop. But the volunteers keep caring for us and our welfare, so we're building the necessary trust.

I like Kentucky because it's so different from Los Angeles or Denver. There aren't distractions of a big city along with the obvious evil temptations. I'm at ease living in horse and bluegrass country and using the time to get myself healed and recovered. It's been truly amazing to watch us women heal in front of each other. I can see the changes occur in front of my eyes, and it's heartwarming and a priceless experience.

2 WEEKS LATER

I've made a friend here, Lori. She's from another part of the country, and it's unlikely we'll have any interaction after we leave this facility. I don't have any qualms talking about my past, so I tell her my whole story. After listening intently for a few hours, she touched on a subject that I hadn't thought about in a long time. She experienced childhood sexual abuse in her past, so it was only natural for her to ask about mine.

"What about you? How are you working through your childhood trauma?" Lori asks.

"Me, what are you talking about?"

She scrunched her shoulders and provided a facial expression that communicated, "Jessica, it's so obvious!"

"Well, I had some stuff happen," I admit and then add, "But it doesn't make me gay."

"Who said anything about being a lesbian?" she asks, surprised at my sexual orientation comment.

"When I was doing pornography, I did some girl-on-girl scenes, and it looked like I was completely into it, but it was just acting. I have no desire for a romantic relationship with a woman."

"Most people know that the sexual delight portrayed in porn is fake, don't they?"

"I hope so!" I quickly respond and giggle.

"Okay, but what does that have to do with your childhood trauma? What happened?"

"Like I said, it didn't make me gay so it isn't a big deal."

"That's not the point and you know it," Lori calmly presses.

"I was just a kid."

"Exactly! None of what happened is your fault. I believe that now," she replied, referring to her own situation, and part of her recovery journey included no longer blaming herself.

"I suppose," I acknowledge. I'm curious to receive her interpretation, so I open up about that part of my childhood.

"When I was in the third grade, I was already five feet, eight inches tall, and of course, they put me on the girls' basketball team. I was an awkward child, and although I wasn't a shy wallflower, attention was thrust on me because of my physical size," I start explaining.

"I wasn't the star of the basketball team; I wasn't blessed with athletic coordination, so even though I was the tallest girl on the court, I wasn't good. Even without my height, my extraverted personality wasn't to blend in; I always stood out and was comfortable knowing that's how God made me."

"I had a friend Tina who was one year older than me," I continue. "She was one of the pretty girls who was also popular, outgoing, and a trendsetter in school. She was *cool and smart* and got along with everyone, students, parents, and teachers alike."

"My friendship with Tina helped me socially because I became popular by my association with her and I saw myself as lucky to be her friend, especially with her being a year older," I admit.

"I was invited many times to stay at her house for a sleepover. I found out later in life that she was molested by her grandfather, but no one knew at the time. She acted out her trauma on me. She repeated what was happening to her. I don't blame her because she was a child too."

"I can't remember the first time it happened, but I remember it occurred on a regular basis. I was too young to comprehend sex

and relationships and liking boys or girls or whatever, but . . ."
I trail off.

"It's okay, Jessica; third graders aren't sexual beings. You weren't mature enough to experience physical attraction," Lori compassionately volunteers.

"Yeah, I know," I start again, take a deep breath, and continue, "She used objects to penetrate me," I utter. It is the first time I told anyone and I wasn't sure how I felt about admitting it.

"How long did this go on?" Lori asks, unfazed.

"It went on for several years until I was about twelve years old; my family moved away, and that's the reason it stopped," I explain.

"And no one ever knew?"

"No, we never got caught; if we heard someone coming up to the bedroom, we'd throw on our clothes or hide under the covers if it were at night. We kept it a secret. I knew what I was doing was wrong, but at that age, I wasn't sure why."

"When I became older, I always wondered if having this relationship with another girl made me gay or not, but when I found out in my twenties that Tina was being abused during this time, it finally made sense to me. It wasn't a sexual attraction situation, but instead, it was Tina reacting to her rape and repeating it on me," I explain and let out a deep breath.

"Well, you may think it's no big deal, but it must have influenced the decisions you made throughout your life," Lori points out and continues, "She was your friend, but maybe you loved and hated her simultaneously? One of the books around here is called *The Wounded Heart*, and you should probably read it sometime."

"Okay, I'll look for it," I answer.

"I'm sure it screwed up your sense of worth and put sex in the center of it," Lori explains. "That's what the counselors told me about my childhood trauma. It might be similar for you."

"Yeah, you're probably right," I answer.

"It sounds like you haven't talked to the counselors about it yet."

"Do you think I should? Is it *that* important?" I ask, and she turns her head slightly and puckers her lips in a facial expression saying, "Duh! Of course, it's important."

15 WEEKS LATER

I recognize that my behavior is changing and being isolated from the rest of the world is necessary. The volunteers know us so well. They know our strengths and weaknesses, and they know what consequences will modify our actions. All of us women are building personal integrity.

My routine and disciplined schedule are good for me, and I look forward to the planned activities. We're learning to communicate, respect personal boundaries, and attend individual and group counseling sessions. The counselors are helping me tie my childhood abuse to decisions I made as an adult. It's been a revelation and is helping me to forgive myself and move forward.

For the longest time, I was rebelling against Jesus, and I closed my heart and mind to Him. I was trying to hurt Him in the only way that I knew, and that was to sin, and sin often to offend Jesus. My actions were purposeful, trying to anger God and corrupt my soul. Let's face it, I achieved my goal.

An important piece of my recovery is daily prayer. There's group and individual prayer time. When I pray, I become closer to Jesus. I want Him to be my friend and my heart has been touched by God. All the women here have different life experiences, but our individual roads lead us to the same cross.

I'm also in regular communication with my parents. After the shock wore off, they've been incredibly supportive, and they constantly pray for me. I am so happy that we've reconciled and returned to a healthy relationship. I draw on their strength and feeling loved by my parents has given me an amazing amount of confidence and motivation. Being in a close relationship with them brightens my attitude, and I know I'm lucky because not all the women here have that parental bond.

I knew then, as I know now, that my actions hurt myself, and for the last decade, I was under the assumption that God had written me off. But He never abandoned me during my time of great sin. He was always there knocking on the door but I refused to let Him in. That's changed, and the entrance is wide open, and I stand in the doorway, inviting Him into my heart and my life.

Being in this refuge enables me to re-establish my relationship with Jesus. I've asked for forgiveness, and He's the ultimate friend. I count on Jesus for anything and everything. Jesus is integral to my healing process. He walks alongside me, side-by-side, hand-in-hand to give me courage. I know that Jesus loves me, not because I'm good, *but because He is good.*

My heart is filled with joy and my love for Jesus. I talk to Him every day. He blesses me with the fortitude to repurpose myself. I'm made for this and I've weathered the storm. None of me was thrown out; I was repaired and improved. Jesus on the cross paid for my sins so I don't have to relive them each day.

I did a little research about my rapist and found out that he was arrested several times and was a serial sex offender. I have forgiven him and prayed that he found Jesus like I have and chose a path of redemption. I have no idea what he did with his life after he raped me all those years ago, but I fear it might be too late for him because I discovered that he's no longer living.

THREE MONTHS LATER

I consider my friend Lori an intelligent woman, but she's talking about leaving the program because she's anxious to return home. When she first told me, I tried to convince her to stay, but she is wavering with her decision.

I feel nervous for her and anxious for me. Can I continue healing without the love and support of my friend? I pray for her and ask Jesus to provide me with guidance. My heart blossoms with peace, and my desire to heal is stronger than being contingent on what someone else does with her life.

I realized why I was selfish for the past decade and I don't want to be that person anymore. I hate the parts that are not healed and my past fuels me to recognize and conquer it.

I start to see myself as courageous. I allow myself to see me as God sees me. That's the most powerful image I can imagine! I'm finally in control of my own destiny and I no longer want to do it alone. I now walk along with God and I feel His presence all the time. *I will never be alone again.*

* * *

We pray for wisdom, Your voice to hear
We cry in anger when we cannot feel You near
We doubt Your goodness, we doubt Your love
As if every promise from Your word is not enough
And all the while, You hear each desperate plea
And long that we'd have faith to believe
'Cause what if Your blessings come through raindrops
What if Your healing comes through tears
What if a thousand sleepless nights are what it takes to
    know You're near

What if trials of this life are Your mercies in disguise
"Blessings" - Laura Story

PART 7, MARCH 2019, GREELEY, CO, AGE 38

I'm out on my own, living a very simple life, typically earning just under $10,000 per year, mostly from speaking engagements. It feels great to steward my life. I spend a lot of time on my parent's farm and our relationship grows stronger. They can't understand why I enjoy chopping wood so much.

I've got a powerful desire deep in my soul, compelling me to inform the public about the immorality I've witnessed that's right under our noses. I've been all over the country making presentations and speaking out against the pornography industry and the sexualization of our children. I've explained the connection pornography has with sex trafficking. I've worked with legislators on these issues, but it is frustrating that many do not see the danger as clearly as I do.

I'm in Greeley tonight to address the school board meeting and the topic is the new Colorado sex education mandate. This is what I told them:

"Thank you for allowing me to speak. While Rights, Respect and Responsibility sounds like a good title, the devil is in the details. Lesson number two for the kindergarten class is where students will be told 'Most people have a vulva and a vagina or a penis and testicles but some people's bodies can be different.' And teachers are to ask, 'Who has a vulva? Girls, boys, or both?' This is health science?" I ask.

"Both boys and girls can have the same body part? This lesson plan is biologically non-factual and is ideologically driven. Despite the insistence that gender is fluid, that's not reality. Teaching this isn't kindergarten age-appropriate at all and screams an indoctrination lesson plan. First grade isn't any better with reading books titled, *My Princess Boy*. Some people don't want tolerance; they want indoctrination and sexualization of the children," I passionately explain.

"I should know because I was once part of the problem. I spent three years working in the pornography industry, normalizing what I'm now ashamed of. I never wanted to see what I saw, and I never wanted to experience what I experienced. Yet kids have access to pornography like never before. It's all connected."

"This hypersexualized curriculum is traumatizing these kids, destroying their innocence," I tell them. I'm looking at the popular school board member with the purple hair, who thinks she is so cool, progressive, and modern. And maybe she's well-meaning, but she is totally clueless, so I continue.

"This curriculum talks about consent but you're not teaching kids how to say *no*, but rather how to get that person to say *yes*. You've got it backwards. It is pushing young teens and children to sexual activity. Don't teach a victim mentality for that will only result in an addiction to those who provide *solutions*," I say and receive mostly blank faces in return.

"You're grooming them. You say you fight for human rights, but that's a code word for child sex rights, which contradicts parental rights. This is pretty disjointed, so I implore you to reject this 3R program," I reply, and I leave it at that.

"Thank you, and let's go to the next speaker," one of the board members respond.

JUNE 2021, AGE 40

I'm living a healthy lifestyle and view myself as somebody who is in recovery and healing. It's a lifelong journey, and I'll never be finished, but I'm in a good place and see myself as a survivor. And don't forget, God loves a comeback story.

I'm walking in downtown Denver with my friend Michael Alarcon after attending a Catholic mass. I met Michael in 2019 at a political conference, and we've become good friends. I left that conference disappointed because they were typical politicians, all talk and no action. That experience led me to actively put pressure on legislators of both parties.

We get in line at a deli when I freeze in place; I see somebody from my past. He looks my way but doesn't appear to recognize me.

Michael notices the guy looking at me, and being his friendly self, says hello to the man.

"Hey," he casually answers and slightly nods his head upwards. He looks at me a half-second longer and turns around to place his order.

It takes forever for his sandwich to be completed, but it arrives at last and he pays for it. I won't engage with him, and I sure won't remind him who I am or introduce him to Michael.

It took an eternity, but he finally leaves the deli. A few minutes later, Michael pays for our lunch, and we walk outside to find a place to eat.

It didn't take long for Michael to ask the obvious question, "Who was that?"

"Someone I used to know in Los Angeles in the porn business."

"Oh," Michael replies, and we're left with a moment of awkward silence.

"I doubt he recognized me," I comment. The first thought that popped into my head was that I wish I were fat, so no one would notice me and I could disappear. I take a deep breath and a sense of calm comes over me. I'm relieved when I realize that I'm going to be okay.

"What's going on in that head of yours?" Michael asks for he could see the wheels spinning inside my brain.

"That was the moment I've feared the most. When someone from my past life appears out of nowhere. I wasn't sure how I would react, but do you know what, I'm not falling apart!" I tell him with glee.

Michael smiles at me and says, "You're strong now. And you're not going back to that dark place again."

"I finally believe that and accept everything that's happened," I tell him.

"Keep the past in the past," Michael says.

I nod at him with self-assurance and say, "My past doesn't define me nor will it destroy me."

"You've gone through so much and instead of being broken, you're determined to live your life."

"You're right–*I have moved on*," I express with gratitude.

I briefly look up to the sky and there was a moment of glare in my eyes from the bright Colorado sunshine, but I distinctly saw the devil out of the corner of my eye, *no longer smiling*.

* * *

Saint Maximilian Kolbe, anticipating the coming invasion by Nazi Germany, July 1939 (emphasis added). Prior to dying in an Auschwitz death camp in 1941, he wrote: "A frightful struggle is coming. Here in Poland, we can expect the worst. We need not worry but must bravely conform our will to Mary Immaculate. The physical sufferings will only help toward making us holier. We should even thank those who torment us. A soft word to hard hearts may convert them. **In short, we are invincible.**"

Jessica Joy has appeared in the documentary film, *Whose Children Are They*

5
IN HER OWN WORDS

BREAHANNAH LEARY

"In April of 2022, I talked to Breahannah about reviewing the book and providing a quote about the book, which she did. She also sent me her own story. With Breahannah's permission, we decided to include her compelling and raw statement, in her voice and her own words." - John DiGirolamo

I am Breahannah Leary and this is my testimony. I remember some of it like it was literally yesterday. Some of it I have fought so hard to keep down and forget. I have attended many years of therapy and many years of psychiatry. I have my good days and I have my bad days, but every day I am blessed.

I am free from a man (I hate calling him a man–he is a poor excuse for a human) that did everything to destroy me and my authentic self. My experience of being a survivor of human sex trafficking has taken me to places I never wish anyone to have to go or be. I have lost all capabilities to want to love or be in a "normal" relationship.

Every time I see a tall black male with long dreads my heart goes to my feet and I get thrown back into the first night I was stuck under my trafficker. I never in my life understood flashbacks or PTSD until I was rescued out of a major sex trafficking ring here in Denver, CO.

I was moved to Phoenix, Arizona, shortly after my rescue to keep me safe from him. I had nights where I would literally believe he was outside my aunt's house, just waiting for me to come outside so he could make me go with him.

He always got what he wanted and if it wasn't handed to him, he would take it. The fear I lived with was not a way of living at all. After being abused mentally, emotionally and physically for many months while under him, I lost all respect for myself and my family believed I was "just a whore who didn't care for her children." That was not the case at all. The day I finally physically got away from him, I called the police on myself from a hotel after meeting a *John*.

My trafficker had received a video of me breaking one of his "rules." He got on the phone with me and said he was on his way to kill me. I truly believed it. After everything I had seen him do to the other women and the horrible things he had done to me, I wasn't about to be some dead hooker blasted all over the news.

I called the police knowing I had a previous warrant for my arrest and I would be taken into custody. I told the arresting officer everything on our ride to Adams County Jail about what he was doing. The officer I like to call Deputy Dewy didn't believe me and assumed I was making up lies to not go to jail. I wanted to go to jail to get away from him but I also wanted him caught, arrested and the rest of the women and young ladies saved.

After my arrest, I was bonded out and went to my uncle's house where I knew I would have been found. I thought at this moment I was free and I wouldn't have to see him again . . . I was wrong. A couple weeks later I got a call from my dad saying the FBI was wanting to speak with me. I was scared and very hesitant to respond. My father insisted I call back the detective. So I did.

My life had been saved when I finally had the courage to go speak with the FBI in person. The detective on the case was very passionate about her job and wanted to put these pimps/traffickers away for the horrible crimes they committed and the many lives they had ruined. I agreed to help her keep track of my trafficker and lie to him, acting as if I knew nothing of the federal government wanting to put this very violent dangerous man behind bars.

I was in Arizona at the time that I remained in contact with my trafficker. I wanted him caught and I wanted all the women that he was brainwashing, manipulating, and keeping them high on substances to be free from his abuse.

I had night terrors every night and I still do all these years later. He was finally indicted and arrested. He was sentenced to hundreds of years in prison after I testified, and the testimonies of many brave young women that also went head-on with this horrible human.

I believed that to be the end and I could finally move on with my life. Little did I know the healing process was just beginning. I started using heavy drugs to keep the horrible memories pushed down and I isolated myself a lot in my room at my aunt's house. If the doorbell would ring, I would literally go into a panic attack believing that my trafficker had sent someone for me. I was afraid of the UPS driver. I kept my head on a swivel at all times. The fear was real.

I would call the detective that was on the case at 3:00 a.m. some nights because the night terrors I was having were so vivid and real that I thought someone was coming to kill me. She was very supportive and would help talk me down from these horrible terrors I was having. Now I am a **survivor** and I continue to advocate for women and young ladies/men who are trying to find a way to heal from the horrific things that these traffickers have traumatized them with.

I have come so far in my recovery and I have now been two years clean from all drugs and I have a job back in nursing. I truly believe that I will never fully forget the horrors of what had happened to me but I do know that I am safe, and I am capable of helping those who think there is no hope left for them.

I wish to help stop human sex trafficking and save at least one victim. I would not have survived if it wasn't for my faith, the help of the FBI and the detective. I am a survivor!

I am free from the horrible days of being forced to sell myself for another one's gain. I am free and alive to tell my story and I am very thankful that I can say I have faced those horrific days of being drugged, and forced to sell my soul to the Devil himself.

I am not very good with my words and I am still trying to fully find ways to help those struggling. I have finally found my voice and I am here to be the voice of those who feel as if they have lost theirs to this horrible issue we have right in our very own backyards.

Many believe that human trafficking is something that happens in big cities or on our borders. The victims are most likely to be someone in your very own family. From the beautiful suburbs to small country towns, it is happening right under our noses, and it needs to be addressed, and awareness needs to be out there.

My story is just one of many hundreds and even thousands. A lot of the victims don't get a chance to tell their story. Sometimes it's just a little too late. These traffickers/pimps will do anything to keep themselves from getting caught, and they often truly silence their victims.

They impregnate their victims and use their children as a pawn in their game to remain in control of their victims. It is never a fairytale story and it's difficult for most to talk about or even hear about.

I am not afraid any longer to help get the word out about these crimes happening right in our very own towns, cities, states, and worldwide.

WHAT CAN YOU DO?

1. **Learn the truth about human trafficking.** Human trafficking is a crime involving the severe exploitation of another person for the purposes of compelled labor or a commercial sex act using force, fraud, or coercion.

   Free online training is available here:

   https://nhttac.acf.hhs.gov/soar/soar-for-individuals/ soar-online

   Read and watch survivor informed and created material as part of your education, including books, blogs, reports, videos, training, and programming. If the information gets over-whelming, listen to the voice of survivors.

2. **Report suspicious behaviors or circumstances.** Be aware of your surroundings and talk about human trafficking with others. Take action when something doesn't look right about a situation you see. A call to ask law enforcement to do a welfare check on someone's well-being is often the appropriate response. Allow trained professionals to assess the situation.

   Put your safety and the safety of a victim first. Do not confront a suspected trafficker.

3. **Connect locally**: Many community-based programs and services offer training, host events, coordinate services for victims, or need volunteers. Look for regional anti-trafficking collaborations in your area to find ways to get involved in your community.

The National Human Trafficking Hotline (https://humantraffickinghotline.org/)

To request help or to report suspected human trafficking, call the hotline: **888-373-7888** or Text BE FREE **(233-733)**. Be informed, learn, and share.

The Colorado Human Trafficking Hotline (https://combathumantrafficking.org/hotline/)

To request help or to report suspected human trafficking, call the hotline: **866-455-5075** or Text **720-999-9724**.

Quick Facts About Sex Trafficking: (Source: www.fromsilencedtosaved.org/hard-facts)

- Average age of entry is 12-14 years old for girls and 11-13 for boys
- On average, one victim can make over $300,000 in revenue for their trafficker. That can mean they are raped anywhere from 15-20 times per day
- Most sex buyers (67%) are white middle-aged men
- The life expectancy of a human trafficking victim is 7 years
- 300,000 children each year are at risk of some form of sexual exploitation
- 60% of children exploited in prostitution are recruited by peers

- The majority of runaways, homeless, abused, and at-risk children are approached by pimps and drug dealers within 48 hours of landing on the streets. That equates to 1 out of 3 being lured into sex trafficking.
- As many as 2.8 million children run away each year in the US
- Children who are sexually abused earlier in childhood are 4× more likely to be targeted and victimized by commercial sexual exploitation
- Pimps use the internet, text messages, and digital web cameras to set up "dates," making them more difficult to find
- It is a crime that hides in plain sight

RECOGNIZING THE SIGNS:

Most Common Work and Living Conditions:

- Person is not free to leave or come and go as he\she wishes, not by force but by fraud and coercion
- Person is under 18 and providing commercial sex acts
- Person is in the commercial sex industry and has a pimp\ manager
- Person is unpaid, paid very little, or paid only through tips
- Works excessively long and\or unusual hours
- Is not allowed breaks or suffers under unusual restrictions at work
- Owes a large debt and is unable to pay it off
- High security measures exist in the work and\or living locations

Most Common Mental, Behavioral or Physical Health Signs:

- Fearful, anxious, depressed, submissive, tense, nervous, or paranoid
- Avoids eye contact
- Sleep-deprived
- Lacks health care and\or is in poor physical condition
- STD and\or pregnancy and\or forced abortion
- Appears malnourished
- Shows signs of physical abuse or confinement
- Shows signs of branding tattoos
- Needs permission for simple decisions, such as going to the restroom
- Drug\alcohol abuse

Other:

- Has few or no personal possessions
- Is not in control of his\her own money
- Is not in control of his\her own identification documents
- Inability to clarify where he\she is living
- Lack of knowledge of whereabouts (does not know what city he\she is in)
- Not in school (if under 18)
- Loss of sense of time
- Unable to speak for themselves
- Living out of a motel or car
- Gang affiliation

Source: https://thisishumantrafficking.com/what-can-you-do/

WHAT DOES HUMAN TRAFFICKING LOOK LIKE?

It may not be visible. It's likely not obvious. And it probably doesn't look like what you've seen portrayed in the movies or on TV. It can't be identified by looking for any one "type" of person, but rather by potential risk factors.

Traffickers often target people who appear vulnerable to exploitation.

There are many contributing and often interrelated factors that can leave someone vulnerable such as:

- Poverty
- Housing insecurity
- Any unstable living environment
- Addiction or substance use
- Lack of support from family, friends
- Lack of access to services

HOW DOES A TRAFFICKER OPERATE?

Traffickers represent people of all races, genders, and social or economic statuses. Often a trafficker is someone the victim knows and trusts such as an intimate partner relationships, employers, friends, and even family members. Traffickers use force, fraud, and\or coercion to trap their victims. Traffickers also create situations where their victims are dependent on them, making it nearly impossible to escape.

A trafficker might:

- Make promises of a better life
- Offer legal status or threaten to turn them over to the police
- Make threats, become violent

Traffickers have many other methods to control their victims such as:

- Isolating from family and friends
- Controlling and monitoring movement
- Continuing to make false promises
- Threatening family members well-being or sharing images of them with friends, family, schools
- Grooming and psychological manipulation and creating a trauma bond

Traffickers also create situations where their victims are dependent on them:

- Withholding basic needs and substances such as food, shelter, and health services
- Putting the victim in a position where they owe their trafficker money (debt-bondage)
- Confiscating documentation and identification (stealing identities, social security numbers for fraudulent and criminal activities)

TIPS FOR PARENTS:

Red Flags for Grooming:

1. New older boyfriend
2. New or unexplained gifts, second cellphone
3. Sudden change in behavior, more defiant
4. Sudden change in dress (more promiscuous)
5. Sudden change in attitude about sex (e.g., no big deal)
6. Secrecy about new friends or boyfriend
7. Sudden drop in grades
8. Starts using drugs or alcohol
9. Missing school or quitting sports\activities
10. Unexplained nights away from home

Ten Ways to Protect Your Child:

1. Talk to your kid and know his\her friends
2. Extracurricular activities and hobbies
3. Know what your kid is doing online
4. It's okay to say "no"
5. Spent time together
6. Be the parent, not the friend
7. Know where they get things you didn't purchase
8. Teach your kid about the world
9. Don't ignore the signs
10. Get counseling when needed

OCCUPATIONAL AWARENESS:

Some professions are more likely to come across a trafficking situation. For example, a construction worker might notice other workers living in unfinished houses. A hotel owner might notice a room that has a lot of activity with multiple people coming and going. Other occupations where you might cross paths with a victim include but are not limited to healthcare workers, restaurant workers, and law enforcement.

If you are suspicious that you or someone you know or have seen is under the control of a trafficker, report. Even if you are unsure, or if you turn out to be mistaken, it is better to make the call because you could save someone's life.

Put your safety and the safety of a victim first. Do not confront a suspected trafficker. Depending on the situation, you may be in a position to ask a few simple questions of the victim, or provide them the hotline number to call **888-373-7888** or Text **BE FREE (233-733).**

ACKNOWLEDGMENTS

I'd like to thank Jenelle Goodrich, Angela Rae Clark, Jessica Joy, and the real Detective Ronald Barnes for sharing their experiences to make this book possible.

I also appreciate my early readers for their input and encouragement, specifically Jennifer Adamson, Geri Frost, Lynn Klopstad, Ted Montoya, Dean Morgan, Brian O'Connell, and Diane Williams.

And finally, to thank my wife and best friend, Kathy for being my biggest cheerleader and first line editor.

ABOUT THE AUTHOR

JOHN DIGIROLAMO

Photograph courtesy of @Mason Strick (Instagram)

John DiGirolamo is an author, speaker, and anti-human trafficking advocate. John wrote the book *It's Not About the Sex* because he believes that human trafficking is one of the most underreported issues of our day, that cuts across all economic, social, racial, and political boundaries. He focused on stories from rural and suburban America, seeking to shine a light on and create awareness of the evils of human trafficking.

DiGirolamo previously wrote *It's Not About the Badge*, a creative nonfiction book that profiles the human side of policing, featuring rural officers. After asking officers about a day on the job they would never forget, the book features compelling personal and professional stories of small-town police officers and has a **5-star rating on Amazon.**

In addition to publishing *It's Not About the Sex*, DiGirolamo previously wrote a newspaper column in the *Sangre De Cristo Sentinel* and *Winter Park Times* and published a collection of short stories, *#12 Suicide*.

DiGirolamo is a retired CPA who worked in various management positions at both small and large technology companies, and currently lives in Chaffee County, CO. Contact John at:

johndtheauthor@gmail.com

and visit the author's website:

http://www.itisnotabout.com/

and Facebook at:

https://www.facebook.com/profile.php?id=100078633528093

Made in the USA
Columbia, SC
14 June 2022